Meat-eaters Versus Vegetarians

Independence
Educational Publishers
Cambridge

First published by Independence
PO Box 295
Cambridge CB1 3XP

© Craig Donnellan 1996

British Library Cataloguing in Publication Data
Meat-eaters Versus Vegetarians – (Issues for the Nineties Series)
I. Donnellan, Craig II. Series
179.3

ISBN 1 86168 002 3

Printed in Great Britain
at Leicester Printers Ltd
Leicester, Great Britain

Typeset by
Claire Boyd

Cover
The illustration on the front cover is by
Katherine Fleming / Folio Collective.

CONTENTS

Introduction

Meat-eaters Versus Vegetarians is the nineteenth volume in the series: **Issues For The Nineties**. The aim of this series is to offer up-to-date information about important issues in our world.

Meat-eaters Versus Vegetarians looks at the ethical and health issues surrounding the food we eat. The information comes from a wide variety of sources and includes:

Government reports and statistics
Newspaper reports and features
Magazine articles and surveys
Literature from lobby groups
and charitable organisations.

It is hoped that, as you read about the many aspects of the issues explored in this book, you will critically evaluate the information presented. It is important that you decide whether you are being presented with facts or opinions. Does the writer give a biased or an unbiased report? If an opinion is being expressed, do you agree with the writer?

Meat-eaters Versus Vegetarians offers a useful starting-point for those who need convenient access to information about the many issues involved. However, it is only a starting-point. At the back of the book is a list of organisations which you may want to contact for further information.

*****

The practice of vegetarianism

The term 'vegetarian' embraces a wide span of definitions, but generally describes a range of diets that exclude all animal flesh (meat, fish and poultry). The restriction of animal-derived ingredients varies greatly and the degree and nature of the exclusion of food items depends principally on the reasons for the decision to adhere to a vegetarian diet.

While the term more accurately describes foods excluded from the diet, the term 'vegetarianism' is often identified with particular food choice patterns additional to the food exclusion. Thus meat may be replaced with either greater quantities of other 'normal' components of a traditional omnivore diet (e.g. more cheese, eggs, bread) or with the introduction of 'replacement' products not typically consumed in a western omnivorous diet (e.g. nut burgers, soya-based products). Considerable care must be taken to clarify the diet/health relationships often discussed in relation to vegetarianism and the dietary differences with an omnivorous diet: are differences observed a result of the exclusion of a dietary component i.e. meat or the inclusion of greater amounts of other dietary components e.g. vegetables, wholemeal bread? Care must also be taken to consider the many non-dietary ('lifestyle') differences that may contribute to the differences in health status sometimes observed.

Types of vegetarian diets

The main types of vegetarian diet are described in Table 1. The restrictiveness of diets adopted is often progressive, in that avoidance of red meat often precedes a decision to become vegetarian, and in turn,

British Nutrition Foundation

most vegans previously followed a vegetarian diet. In a study of different vegetarian groups in London (Draper *et al*, 1993), 65% of vegans had previously been lacto-ovo vegetarian, whereas only 4% of the lacto-ovo vegetarians had previously been vegan. The study indicated, however, that the length of time of adherence to the diet at the time of being asked was shortest for vegans (one year) followed by lacto-ovo vegetarians (two years) and demi-vegetarians (five to nine years).

Reasons for vegetarianism

The degree of animal-product exclusion, and the period of time people typically state that they have followed a vegetarian diet, will depend largely on the reasons for this dietary practice. The most important reasons are:

Religion

Several religions require vegetarianism or condemn the consumption of certain foods: most typically these are the flesh of particular animals (see Table 2). Hindus are prohibited from consuming any flesh from a cow, as this animal is considered sacred. In contrast, pork may not be consumed in some religions e.g. Islam or Judaism because it is considered to be unclean because of its scavenging habits; shellfish and other marine scavengers may not be eaten for the same reason. In some instances very strict criteria govern the conditional consumption of certain types of meat, usually requirements that relate to the method of slaughter, and people may choose to avoid the consumption of

Table 1: Main types of vegetarian diets	
Diet	**Description**
'Semi' or Demi-vegetarian ('meat avoiders')	Exclusion of red meat. Occasional consumption of fish/poultry.
Vegetarian (lacto-ovo)	Exclusion of all meat, fish and poultry and ingredients derived from these sources e.g. gelatine, rennet. Consumption of dairy products and eggs.
Vegan	Exclusion of all animal derived products and ingredients.
Macrobiotic	Exclusion of all meat and dairy products and eggs. Occasional use of (mainly lean) fish. Progressive levels of the diet become increasingly restrictive with gradual elimination of all animal-origin foods, fruit and vegetables. At the final level, only brown rice is eaten.

all meat products where adherence to the specified criteria cannot be guaranteed. Most people avoiding certain types of meat for religious reasons will have followed this practice throughout their entire lives.

Moral and ethical beliefs
In many cases, the main reason given for a decision to avoid meat is an objection to killing animals and/or concerns over animal welfare during rearing and transport. Concerns over 'modern' animal production techniques are also indicated as reasons why a few vegetarians choose to further exclude dairy products or 'battery' eggs from their diets.

Economical and ecological considerations
Diets low in animal proteins are typically less expensive than meat-based diets. This factor is of particular significance in many of the near-vegetarian diets consumed in some developing countries and is less likely to be a primary issue in Western countries. However, the vegetarian diet is also considered to be more 'efficient' in the provision of energy and nutrients in the context of limited world food resources and high population growth rates. A related argument promoted more recently has been the destructive nature of mass animal production techniques in relation to ecological concerns.

Health
Vegetarian diets are often described as 'healthier' in relation to the achievement of dietary targets and nutrient reference values. Meat products can be high in total fat and saturated fatty acids, and meat 'avoidance' is often viewed as the most simple way to achieve a 'healthier' diet: the extent to which this is true will depend greatly on the nutritional profile of the foods consequently consumed in greater quantities.

In practice, people choosing to become vegetarian are likely to be motivated by several reasons. Surveys of UK subjects indicate that the principal factors in deciding to become vegetarian are moral/ethical. Beliefs in the health benefits of vegetarianism are usually described as being of secondary importance, and are often 'additional' but not 'principal' reasons for becoming vegetarian (Carlson *et al*, 1985; Leatherhead Food RA, 1994; Draper *et al*, 1990).

Trends in vegetarianism

Although vegetarianism has been practised in the UK throughout recent history, the proportion of people following a vegetarian diet is probably higher than at any previous time (see Table 3), although the figures post-1990 appear to be stable at about 3 to 4% of adults. There are many reasons, but major factors are probably the immigration of groups of people who avoid certain meat products for religious reasons, the widespread availability and quality of alternative foods, and the increased public concerns over animal welfare issues. The assessment of trends in vegetarianism will depend on definitions used, including criteria on:
- 'strictness' of exclusion of meat/ animal products
- duration of exclusion practice.

A survey by a UK market research company on behalf of a manufacturer of vegetarian foods (Realeat), demonstrated a gradual increase in the number of adults describing themselves as vegetarian in the ten years from 1984. There was an even larger increase in the percentage of adults who claim to be avoiding red meat.

Vegetarianism was particularly high in young women, and was higher in the South (4.5%) compared to the North (3.6%) and Scotland (1.4%) (Realeat, 1993). Clarification of definitions is important where comparisons between surveys are made: studies of food diaries show that in some cases 'vegetarian' subjects do consume some animal flesh products (Wright & Howcroft, 1992).

Table 2: Food exclusion in religious groups

X = Foods avoided S = Specific criteria may apply	Pork	Beef	Lamb	Chicken	Fish
Hindu	X	X	S	S	S
Muslim	X	Halal only	Halal only	Halal only	S
Sikh	X	X	S	S	S
Jewish	X	Kosher only	Kosher only	Kosher only	S
Buddhist (strict)	X	X	X	X	X
Seventh-Day Adventist	X	X	X	S	S
Rastafarian	X	X	X	X	X

Table 3: Adult vegetarians in the UK

	Vegetarians	Avoid/rarely eat meat	Sample
1984	2.1%	1.9%	Adults 16+
1988	3.0%	5.5%	Adults 16+
1990	3.7%	6.3%	Adults 16+
1993	4.3%	6.5%	Adults 16+
1995	4.5%	7.3%	Adults 16+
Source: Gallup on behalf of Realeat Foods Ltd (n=4000)			
1988	1%	8%	Female 16-64
1990	2%	13%	Female 16-64
1992	3%	10%	Female 16-64
1994	3%	9%	Female 16-64
Source: National Health Survey (Jones Rhodes Associates) (n=900)			
1990	2%	8%	Adults 16+
1994	3%	9%	Adults 16+
Source: Taylor Nelson Family Food Panel (n = 3–4000)			
1993	2%	6%	Adults 18+
Source: Leatherhead Food RA (n= 500)			

Studies in Cardiff and London have shown that vegetarians are more likely to be from social classes 1 and 2, and are more likely to have attended university, than non-vegetarians (Shickle *et al*, 1989; Draper *et al*, 1993).

Health-related beliefs and lifestyle of vegetarians

People choosing to exclude meat-products from their diets are also more likely to modify other aspects of their lifestyle; these other health-related behaviours might represent a 'clustering' of practices that may have an important effect on health, quite apart from meat exclusion.

In the Cardiff survey of 90 vegetarians (Shickle *et al*, 1989), there were slightly more non-smokers and/or non-drinkers, than in non-vegetarian groups. Vegetarians who smoked, did so less frequently, whereas vegetarians who consumed alcohol did so more frequently than non-vegetarians. Differences between groups in the amount of exercise taken were not evident.

Vegetarians appear to be more likely to consume nutritional supplements, even though they consider their diets to be 'healthier' than omnivores (Freeland-Graves *et al*, 1986). Vegans were more likely to consider that their diets fully supplied all the vitamins they needed: 67% versus 57% of vegetarians – however vegans were also more likely than vegetarians to consume nutritional supplements: 54% versus 41% (Draper *et al*, 1993). National data indicate lower levels of supplement taking – about 10% of British adults (Gregory *et al*, 1990). A study of Dutch vegetarians similarly indicated a much higher percentage of subjects who used vitamin C supplements (25%) as compared to Dutch omnivores (3%) (van Faassen *et al*, 1993).

Some of the differences in health-related behaviour in vegetarian groups may be due to differences in knowledge and attitudes. The Cardiff survey (Shickle *et al*, 1989), showed a greater nutritional knowledge in vegetarians and interestingly, a greater desire for more information on nutrition, than in the non-vegetarian groups. Vegetarians appear more likely to believe in the relationship between diet and health (Freeland-Graves *et al*, 1986; Draper *et al*, 1990), and tended to be less 'fatalistic' about health than non-vegetarians. This may explain some of the differences observed in vegetarians other than differences attributed principally to meat-exclusion.

People excluding one or more meat products from their diets for religious reasons may also have different practices in relation to the consumption of other foods or drinks: Seventh-Day Adventists in the United States, who typically exclude meat from their diet, are also prohibited from the consumption of alcoholic drinks, caffeine-containing beverages and from smoking. Avoidance of alcohol in particular is also observed by Muslims and Buddhists. These lifestyle factors have to be considered when assessing the attributes of vegetarian diets.

● The above is an extract from *Vegetarianism – Briefing Paper*, published by the British Nutrition Foundation. For further information about all BNF publications, please contact the Publications Officer at The British Nutrition Foundation. See page 39 for address details.

© British Nutrition Foundation February, 1995

Animal transport

Information from Compassion in World Farming Trust

Introduction

The public has been concerned about the export of live farm animals from the UK for the last 25 years. Despite years of campaigning by CIWF and others, the problem is getting worse. In recent times the concern has become so great that thousands of people, of all ages and backgrounds, in Britain and other European countries, have taken to the streets to protest about the cruelty of these long journeys and to call for an end to the suffering.

Where are animals transported?

After leaving the farm animals may be taken to a market, slaughterhouse or another country. At markets animals are sometimes cruelly treated during loading and unloading. Sticks may be used to hit and jab animals to make them move. Markets are noisy, smelly and frightening places for animals. Some animals are sold to dealers at markets who export them to other countries. Most British sheep are exported to France, with most calves going to Holland or France. However, some British animals may travel as far as Spain, Portugal, Italy and Greece. Some of these journeys may take several days.

What are these journeys like for the animals?

Animals are not used to being transported so the journey can be very stressful for them. Overcrowding is a common problem with animals being tightly packed together. If animals fall over they may be unable to get up and then may be trampled by other animals. In high temperatures, animals may suffer heat exhaustion and even die. Pigs in particular suffer in high temperatures

as they are unable to sweat. If only a few animals are in a truck without proper partitions they may be thrown around in the lorry and suffer various injuries as vehicles brake, take corners too fast, etc. In winter, animals also suffer from the cold. Animals are very often deprived of food, water and rest on these long journeys abroad. Unloading in some continental countries can be a brutal process

with animals being handled very roughly and the use of electric goads being commonplace.

How long are the journeys?

Journeys may be short if animals are just going to the local slaughterhouse, but increasingly even within the UK, journeys to slaughterhouses may be many hours. Animals travelling from the UK across Europe may travel more than 40 hours, sometimes without any food, water and rest, through varying temperature zones.

Why are live animals transported?

Some animals are sent for further fattening and calves usually end up

Unloading in some contin-ental countries can be a brutal process with animals being handled very roughly

in narrow veal crates which are so cruel that their use is illegal in the UK (See Farm Facts: Veal). Most animals are sent for slaughter. Many Europeans say they prefer 'fresh' meat so they want live animals to be slaughtered in their country. Continental traders can also make a bigger profit on the meat by describing it as 'home-killed'. It is absurd that animals should be subjected to the misery of long journeys only to be slaughtered at the journey's end. CIWF would like to see animals sent to slaughter houses as near as possible to the farm on which they are reared. There is absolutely no reason (apart from profit and greed) why this could not happen. Modern vehicles with chilling facilities could then deliver chilled fresh meat throughout Europe.

How many animals are exported each year?

In 1993, Britain exported about 2 million sheep and lambs and around 500,000 young calves. Britain also exported 88,000 pigs in the same year. These figures do not include animals exported for breeding purposes.

How many animals are exported from Ireland?

In 1994, Ireland exported 135,000 pigs, 276,000 sheep and lambs and 403,000 cattle Of the cattle exports 273,000 (62%) were sent to countries outside the EU mainly Egypt, with others going to Libya. The journeys to North Africa and the Middle East are particularly worrying as the cattle have a long journey of 12 -14 days. These sea journeys often encounter rough weather. The trade in cattle to countries outside the EU is supported by subsidies – that is tax payers' money. Ireland also exports calves to Belgium, France, Holland, Italy and Spain.

What laws protect the animals?

Under a new European Union Law calves can travel up to 20 hours (with a one-hour break in the middle of the journey) before getting a 24-hour rest period. Sheep and cattle can travel for 30 hours (again, with a one-hour break in the middle of the journey) and pigs can travel for 26 hours before they receive 24 hours' rest. In all cases, these are not maximum journey times because the journey can be resumed after 24 hours' rest. These new laws come into force at the end of 1996.

What should be done?

Compassion in World Farming is campaigning for:

● animals to be slaughtered as near as possible to the farm where they are reared and only meat to be exported. In other words, the live export trade to be replaced by a carcass-only trade.

● a maximum journey limit of 8 hours for all animals being sent for slaughter or further fattening.

● animals to be treated with respect and classified as 'sentient beings' (animals capable of feeling) under European Union Law. At the moment, they are classed as agricultural products like potatoes or cabbages.

What you can do

If you are interested in campaigning for the welfare of farm animals, join CIWF's Young Supporters Group. It's FREE! Send us your full name, address and date of birth and we'll enrol you. You will then receive our colour newsletter *FarmWatch* and be kept up to date with our campaigns.

Tell your friends about the information on this fact sheet and get them to join CIWF's Young Supporters Group too.

Ask your MP and MEP to do all in his/her power to end the suffering on these long-distance journeys and to ensure that there is a maximum 8 hour journey limit throughout the EU. Your MP can be contacted c/o The House of Commons, London SE1A 0AA. Your MEP's address is: The European Parliament, Rue Belliard, 97 – 113 B – 1047 Brussels, Belgium.

Help us to help farm animals. Together we can make a difference to their lives.

● The above article is from *Farmfacts* published by the CIWF Trust. See page 39 for address details.

© CIWF Trust

CWS Retail ethical purchasing survey 1995

Gallup poll of 30,000 people

- 71% feel retailers had a responsibility to animals
- 70% rank environmental issues as a major concern
- 62% want clearer, more informative labels on products
- 30% claim to have boycotted a store or product on ethical grounds
- Three in five are willing to pay more for goods meeting ethical standards – up to 77p extra for goods costing £10

| 0 | 10 | 20 | 30 | 40 | 50 | 60 | 70 | 80 | % |

The transportation of live animals

Information from the National Farmers' Union

What is the NFU's view on the export of live animals?

To answer that clearly we need to establish what is meant by the term 'live exports'. We fly and ship pedigree animals to other countries without any problems whatsoever.

We fly horses across the world which go on to win races without any upset to their health or welfare.

Sheep and calves are also sent to other EU member states for further fattening or for slaughter. The great majority of these animals arrive in good health after perfectly normal journeys.

The export of all these animals is tightly controlled by laws which stipulate how much food, water, rest and care should be given during each journey. These laws are based on extensive scientific evidence and are fully and unequivocally supported by the NFU.

It is said that animals exported for slaughter or fattening are subjected to appalling suffering. How can the NFU support such a cruel trade?

Carried out properly and within the law, transporting live animals is not cruel. Government vets monitor each and every export consignment and liaise with their counterparts in the receiving country over the animals' condition on arrival.

In saying that, it is true that in a small number of cases, some hauliers and exporters have put their own desire for profit before the welfare of their animals. Their actions are totally unacceptable. The NFU is determined that there must be no hiding place for anyone who fails to

treat an animal with respect. Prosecution and severe punishment must result.

So you won't be joining in calls for a ban on live exports, then?

The NFU is committed first and foremost to ensuring that all animals are treated with care and compassion.

We will not be calling for a ban. We firmly believe that it is possible to continue this very important, legitimate trade without compromising animal welfare.

The UK cannot impose a ban in any case. Such unilateral action would contravene European law.

You say you are opposed to animal cruelty, yet you stand by and watch British calves suffer in foreign veal crates; isn't that hypocrisy?

British farmers cannot be held responsible for systems which are legal elsewhere in Europe.

The use of veal crates was banned in the UK in 1990. The NFU believes firmly that the UK's humane standards of veal calf rearing must be adopted throughout Europe as soon as possible. We are working to achieve this end and develop new market opportunities here in the UK for calves which are surplus to requirements.

But there are over 500,000 calves exported every year – how could they be used in this country?

We would much prefer to rear our own animals in this country. The NFU is looking closely at promoting new production systems for home produced veal, where the animals come from loose housed farms in which they can move around freely and eat roughage.

We are also looking at the production of 'light' beef in which the animal is slaughtered at a younger age than it would be for traditional beef stock.

We are actively canvassing support for both these initiatives from the Meat and Livestock Commission and the Ministry of Agriculture as well as leading food retailers, hotel and restaurant chains. With a strong level of commitment to home produced supplies, we could stamp out the need for imports of veal often produced in systems banned in this country.

In addition to our work on humane veal and 'light' beef, we are looking to develop new export markets for carcase meat. We believe it is far better to export chilled and frozen cuts where possible, although we acknowledge many European customers prefer to slaughter their meat locally.

If people on the Continent want to eat our animals, why not insist they take them in carcase form?
We do export a lot of meat already – of our exports to France, for example, 80% goes as chilled or frozen cuts, with 20% in the form of live animals.

If satisfactory markets can be developed, all animals bred for meat would be slaughtered in this country as close as possible to the farm where they were reared. That is certainly the NFU's objective.

But some Continental consumers will buy only meat which has been killed in their own country. This is particularly true of the French who have very different techniques of butchering from those used here.

We cannot insist – we can only persuade.

What do you think about the violence which has erupted recently at ports exporting live animals?
We reject violence. The way to resolve a difficult issue is by rational discussion and, sometimes, compromise. That is what we are trying to achieve in all our lobbying work. The key to resolving this lies with Europe and the need to implement common welfare standards across the EU.

No one likes to think of animals suffering in any way. We understand the public's concern because we, as farmers, are also concerned. But blocking a lawful trade by violent and unlawful means must never be allowed to succeed.

Are you hoping that the major ferry companies will agree to carry live animals again?
The bans imposed by the major ferry companies are very regrettable. The NFU takes seriously the blatant law breaking by some hauliers which precipitated the bans.

We were particularly saddened that the restrictions were introduced just as the Minister was taking steps to tighten the law and the NFU was

itself in discussion with the ferry companies on the future of the trade.

Obviously we would like to see the ferry trade resumed and we are in constant touch over this possibility. We have secured a commitment from each of them that their actions will be reviewed when there is hard evidence that the new laws designed to protect livestock in transit are working.

What new laws are those?
New controls were introduced by the Government in January this year. They set out a framework for resting, feeding and watering of all livestock in transit and for legal action which can be taken if the rules are breached.

All hauliers must submit a formal journey plan to Government vets which they must stick to. Anyone who makes a false declaration or fails to adhere to their plan without reasonable excuse will be prosecuted through the county courts.

The NFU fully supports these measures which were drawn up by the Government after consultation with us. In fact, it was at the behest of the NFU that the measures were made even tougher. It is essential to crack down hard on those who break the law.

Why can't you just put a brave face on it and accept that the export of live animals is history?
Because we do not believe that has to be the case. It may be that the traditional routes by passenger ferry have been restricted, but there is no

reason why a designated shipping or air line should not be able to operate to satisfactory welfare rules.

Why are you so concerned to protect this trade?
The British livestock industry is very important to the economy as a whole. Closing off an important export market could hit many farmers hard – particularly in the hills and uplands.

Here the live export trade is often the backbone of the local auction market. Without this trade, many farmers would suffer severe difficulties and could be forced out of business.

So the NFU is more concerned with pandering to the demands of the Continental customer than it is with improving conditions for animals?
Of course not. But it must be acknowledged that there is a huge demand for high quality British meat which commands a price premium on many Continental markets.

To ignore that would put many British farming businesses in financial jeopardy and threaten the safety of thousands of jobs in the meat sector.

What we must do as an industry is to work together to ensure that animal welfare is not compromised as we attempt to meet demand in the single European market.
● The above is from a series of factsheets produced by the NFU Public Affairs Department. See page 39 for address details.

© National Farmers' Union
February, 1995

Factory farming

Information from Compassion in World Farming Trust

Introduction

The traditional view of farming is green fields full of grazing animals, or animals lying in straw in barns, with hens scratching around in the farmyard. Sadly, this picture is far removed from the reality of life on the modern farm. The vast majority of farm animals never see the daylight or feel the sun on their backs. Millions of animals spend their entire lives in cages, stalls or huge, windowless sheds where they can barely move. The cramped conditions in which thousands of animals can be kept in one building is known as factory farming.

What is factory farming?

The term 'factory farming' is used to describe very intensive forms of farming where the animals are kept in cramped conditions where they are unable to carry out their natural behaviours. The animals are treated as little more than production machines – hence the term 'factory farming'.

Which farm animals are kept like this?

Laying hens, broiler chickens, turkeys, pigs (breeding sow and fattening pigs), dairy cattle, and even fish, are usually kept in factory farm conditions.

How are hens kept?

Nearly 90% of laying hens are kept in the battery cage system for their entire lives. The cages are so small that they cannot even stretch their wings. They are unable to scratch at the ground, perch, dustbathe or make a nest. Thirty million birds are kept like this in the UK.

What about chickens reared for meat?

Meat birds are called broiler chickens and in the UK we rear over 600 million birds each year. Although these birds are not kept in cages they are still reared in very crowded conditions. Tens of thousands of birds are crammed into windowless sheds where they are forced to grow at twice their natural rate. As a result, many will suffer bone deformities and lameness before being slaughtered at just six weeks old.

How are turkeys reared?

Most turkeys are reared in a similar way to broiler chickens. Millions of turkeys are also crammed into windowless sheds. They often have part of their beaks cut off to prevent aggression. They may suffer from painful breast blisters and ulcerated feet due to standing on filthy floor litter (woodshavings soaked in turkey droppings).

How are most pigs kept?

Some breeding sows are still kept in confined stalls during their 16-week pregnancy. The stalls do not allow the sow to turn around and, in some cases, sows are tethered to the concrete floor. (However, thanks to CIWF, sow stalls and tethering of pigs is being phased out in the UK and will be illegal as from 1st January 1999). The farrowing crate is where the majority of sows will give birth (80% of sows in the UK). The crate is narrower than the sow stall and makes it difficult for the sow to lie down quickly.

The sow is unable to build a nest for her piglets or turn around. Young pigs are fattened in crowded conditions, often in semi-darkness with very little opportunity for movement or play.

Are dairy cows kept intensively?

The modern dairy cow is being pushed to breaking point to produce ever more milk. Most of these animals will spend the winter indoors in cubicles. Dairy cattle frequently suffer from mastitis (painful inflammation of the udder)

The vast majority of farm animals never see the daylight or feel the sun on their backs

and lameness. In order to produce milk, the cows have to give birth to calves. The majority of male calves are still being sent to cruel veal crates in France and Holland. Many cows are worn out by the age of five or six years. Some dairy cattle are kept indoors all year round. This is known as 'zero grazing'. The cows do not graze, instead silage (fermented grass) and high protein feeds are brought to them.

How are fish factory farmed?

Salmon and trout are now also farmed in cages or pens, where they are crowded together. The cages are suspended in lakes, loch or coastal waters. These conditions are totally unnatural and often lead to the fish becoming stressed or diseased.

How do animals suffer on factory farms?

Animals suffer in a variety of ways on factory farms. These include:

- Frustration of natural ('normal') behaviours, e.g. hens being unable to perch, dustbathe or make a nest.
- Being deprived of social contact/ behaviour, e.g. isolation of sows in the farrowing crate.
- Overcrowded conditions, e.g. broiler chickens are crammed together in huge sheds and battery hens in cages.
- Physical discomfort and pain, e.g. from standing on concrete or wire mesh.
- Pushing animals to their physical limits, e.g. broiler chickens being forced to grow so quickly they suffer leg problems and dairy cattle being forced to produce large quantities of milk and being worn out in just a few years.

What you can do

1. If you would like to receive CIWF Trust's youth newsletter *Farm-Watch*, all you need to do is send us your name, full postal address and date of birth. It's FREE so write to us without delay and you'll be put on our mailing list to receive *FarmWatch* each term.
2. Tell your friends about the information on this factsheet and get them to send for *FarmWatch* too.
3. Try to get these issues discussed at your school or youth group and help raise awareness about the plight of farm animals in factory farm conditions.
4. Try to avoid meat and dairy produce resulting from factory farmed animals. Look out for welfare-friendly products, especially organic and free-range. You might like to try alternatives to meat and dairy products.

5. Write to your MP regarding your concerns about the way animals are reared on 'factory farms'. Ask what he/she is doing to improve conditions for farm animals and to support measures to improve farm animal welfare. You can contact your MP c/o The House of Commons, London SW1A 0AA.

© CIWF Trust

Animal welfare

From the Meat and Livestock Commission

Strict legislation is laid down by the British Government and by the EC covering the welfare of sheep, cattle and pigs. Britain's farmers care for their animals in the same way as responsible consumers care for their pets.

We have an outstanding animal welfare record and are very sensitive to consumer perceptions of welfare. For example, Britain outlawed building new sow stalls and tethers from October 1991 and wants them phased out by the end of 1997.

Calves in this country have been reared in group housing on wholesome diets for some years. As a result, the industry agreed with Government when it wished to ban veal crates in January 1990.

The vast majority of lambs spend their whole lives outdoors and the vast majority of beef cattle graze outside between spring and the start of the winter. Indeed, they only come inside when the weather is really bad.

The pig is an animal with little fur and, like a human, must be kept warm so mostly pigs are housed in appropriate surroundings. Nevertheless, an increasing number of pigs are bred outdoors and many sows are now kept in deep straw yards, providing the warmth they need.

Every animal should be reared according to a set of strict welfare codes developed by the UK's Farm Animal Welfare Council and policed by the Government. Like the Highway Code, failure to abide by them can be indicative of guilt and offenders can be heavily punished.

The welfare of livestock during transportation to the Continent has aroused press coverage. In fact, most live exports are just over the water to France and the Netherlands. In the event of any breaches in welfare, punitive disciplinary action is taken and exporters' licences are revoked.

When livestock are in transport their welfare is the responsibility of the country the animals are passing through. The British Government is pressing for the same high welfare standards that operate in the UK to apply throughout Europe.

© Meat and Livestock Commission

Animal welfare

From the National Farmers' Union

Why has the NFU decided to review its welfare policy now?

The public's awareness of food and its production has grown considerably over the past few years. The public has shown great interest in animal welfare issues and we take their concerns seriously especially as there is evidence that the welfare of farm animals plays an increasingly important part in how the consumer views the way their food is produced.

The NFU felt it was appropriate to review its animal welfare policy which has been in existence for a number of years.

The result of this was the working party set up under the chairmanship of former NFU President Sir Simon Gourlay earlier this year.

So, the report is basically a knee jerk reaction from farmers running scared from the recent scenes at Shoreham and Brightlingsea?

No. Farmers and growers produce to very high standards – indeed, some of the strictest standards in the world. They also listen to the consumers who buy the goods they produce – and the report produced by the Gourlay Group is the latest result of this ongoing process.

So what does the report aim to do?

It aims to establish the underlying principles of NFU welfare policy, to identify key welfare issues and policing and to highlight areas of possible improvement. This report also suggests possible measures that could be taken to improve welfare and on-farm care.

Let's get down to specifics. The report implies that the NFU is calling for a maximum journey time of 24 hours – that's more than the 15 hours the NFU previously went along with, isn't it?

:Representing Farmers and Growers

Let's be clear on this. The NFU is NOT calling for a maximum journey time of 24 hours.

The 15-hour rule that has been applied in the UK embraces all species. Recent research suggests that different travelling times could apply to different animals.

Scientific and veterinary evidence is evolving all the time on animal stress and welfare during transport.

We are studying closely the implications of the decision reached by EU Agriculture Ministers at their Council in Luxembourg in June which sets out different journey times according to the age of the animals.

So, what effect will the European decision have on the transport of live animals?

The European deal will take time to work out, but the NFU is consistently working to ensure live exports can continue as a lawful trade but with the strict welfare standards prevailing.

If further scientific research in future pointed to the need to review a particular maximum journey time, then, the NFU would review its policy.

I see the NFU has now entered the religious slaughter debate. But what right does the NFU have to dictate on the requirements of religious slaughter?

Let's be clear on this one. The focus of this report relates to the practical issue of animal welfare.

We are not taking a view on, or judging, religious beliefs. But we are

saying that failure to stun animals before slaughter is seen by the NFU as a practical welfare problem that needs to be addressed.

But by saying this, isn't the NFU, in effect, entering into a religious debate?

We are fully prepared to discuss this whole issue in a constructive and positive way with religious leaders.

Why does the NFU want a labelling system for meat derived from animals slaughtered by religious methods?

To enable consumers to make an informed choice about the meat they purchase.

The report also wants to see more education and training with animal welfare part of any qualifying examination for all those involved in animal welfare from farm to abattoir. But less than 10% of farmers signed up for a mandatory certificate in handling OPs. This is really a waste of time, isn't it?

Not at all. The NFU is consistently working hard to convince its members that it is in their business interests to formalise and update their on-farm training. Such training is essential and must figure prominently in livestock farming.

In this report the NFU is calling for the existing range of education and training schemes in the livestock industry to be reviewed.

But farmers are always complaining that their industry is one of the most regulated and bureaucratic in existence. Surely more red tape will just add to their burden?

The NFU has consistently called for unnecessary red tape to be cut but certain regulations are necessary. Our welfare legislation allows us to demonstrate that British animal welfare is among the best in the world.

The NFU says lameness in dairy cattle is a big problem – and most of the reasons given in the report seem to relate to bad practice by farmers – this rather gives the lie to the NFU's oft-repeated statement that UK farmers are among the most welfare-friendly in Europe, doesn't it ?

Welfare organisations agree that the UK is among the best in Europe for on-farm standards – but the NFU is always looking to pinpoint areas where these standards can be improved.

Lameness is a serious problem and is one area where there is room for improvement. The NFU will be working hard to raise farmers' awareness of the need to continue to improve herd management.

The report mentions animals as 'sentient beings' – but the Treaty of Rome, which covers live export legislation, defines animals as 'agricultural products'. The NFU is therefore advocating a change in the law, isn't it?

For the legal purposes of the Treaty, animals are defined as 'agricultural products'. The NFU regards it as a separate fact that they are creatures capable of feeling pain, fear and fatigue.

The report makes mention of the 'industry' funding welfare research – how can farmers make their financial contributions when the NFU consistently tells us certain livestock sectors are already pushed to the financial brink by live export bans and unilateral welfare legislation?

The Gourlay report sets out the broad principles of the NFU's animal welfare policy and is meant to act as a catalyst for future debate.

Government must properly take the lead in further welfare R&D but there will be occasions where the livestock industry as a whole or parts of it can assist.

The report recommends that farmers think before tail docking and castrating animals. Why is this done in the first place?

Tail docking of lambs prevents infection caused by faeces on the tail, while castration of male lambs enables the farmer to control flock numbers. Piglets have their tails docked to discourage them biting each other.

These procedures are carried out by experienced farmers.

The report recommends that farmers consider whether such operations are necessary on a routine basis, and calls for more research into the management of these procedures.

The report says the NFU has a role to play in passing on information and translating welfare research into on-farm practice. How does it intend to do this?

This will be a subject for future discussion with relevant staff, Council and committee members arising from further debate of the report. Possible avenues could include seminars for members or training courses.

The report also claims the NFU must do more to explain animal welfare issues to the public. That's an admission that the NFU has failed in this respect, isn't it?

No. Independent research carried out over the past few months has shown that the public's perception of farmers has improved since the early 1990s.

This shows that farmers are more willing to answer the public's questions and to explain why certain farming practices have a role in modern agriculture.

The report indicates that animal welfare is an area of growing public concern, and that the NFU should think about how it can best explain what farmers do on their farms and why they do it.

Okay, how does the NFU think it can do that?

This report from the welfare working group is a start in identifying a broad approach. It does not at this stage seek to detail every future step. But the whole issue will be looked at by relevant NFU committees.

One area that could possibly be expanded is the NFU's extremely successful 'open farms' initiative, where members of the public can see commercially orientated farms in practice.

This report is all well and good, but when does the NFU want to see these changes or suggestions taken up?

The NFU has consistently said that welfare legislation must be based on sound science and research – this will take time to come to the fore. We support the ongoing programme of the Farm Animal Welfare Council which ensures a continual review of animal management practices.

The details will be the subject of further ongoing discussions – both with different livestock sectors and other organisations.

● The above is from a series of factsheets produced by the NFU Public Affairs department. See page 39 for address details.

© National Farmers' Union
June, 1995

Realeat Gallup Survey February 1995

A survey of 4237 over 16-year-olds in Britain

- 4.5% of population is vegetarian
- 7.3% of population avoid red meat
- 12.4% of 16-24 year old females are vegetarian
- 3.2% of male population is vegetarian
- 5.8% of female population is vegetarian
- 26% of population eat red meat only occasionally

| 0 | 5 | 10 | 15 | 20 | 25 | 30 % |

Reading the welfare labels

New green and animal-friendly labels have appeared on supermarket meats. But how can consumers know what they are buying? We take a closer look under the wrappers to see what the labels really mean

Concern about animal rearing practices has led many consumers to pay a premium for meat produced to higher standards than typical factory farm products. Supermarkets have been quick to jump on the 'green' bandwagon and a bewildering range of labelling schemes declaring environmentally and animal-friendly credentials have appeared. Words like 'free-range', 'organic', 'traditional', 'heritage' and 'farmhouse' conjure up images of contented animals living in rural bliss. However, the truth may not always be so idyllic and standards can vary between the different schemes.

Organic

To carry an 'organic' label, producers and retailers should ensure that strict standards, covering meat production from the farm to the shop are adhered to, with an audit trail that can be traced back to the farm. EC organic livestock standards are expected to be enshrined in law later this year.

The main organic certifying body is the Soil Association and its standards guarantee that animal feed must be organically grown and pesticide-free, the routine use of drugs and growth promoters is not allowed and stocking densities must be kept low with animals able to graze outdoors. Battery cages for hens and farrowing crates for sows are not permitted, neither are debeaking of hens and tail docking of piglets. Standards also cover animal transport and slaughterhouses.

The Soil Association sets its farmers additional environmental standards through its Guidelines for Conservation.

Products labelled 'organic' which do not bear a Soil Association or similar certification may not have been independently inspected. In such cases the producers are responsible for complying with the organic food regulations and, as with any labelling claim, it would be up to local trading standards officers to prosecute if they have evidence of false labelling.

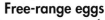

Organic meat is available in a limited number of Sainsbury and Safeway stores, and the supermarkets say they can't get hold of enough stocks to supply more shops. A full list of independent butchers selling organic meat and mail order suppliers is available from the Soil Association.

The Real Meat Company

The Real Meat Company supplies meat and meat products that have been produced to its own Codes of Diet and Welfare which include transport and slaughter (the company uses only 2 slaughter houses, one for chickens and one for mammals). The farm addresses are available to customers and medication is permitted only in cases of actual illness and with double the normal withdrawal period. A key difference from 'organic' is that Real Meat Company standards do not insist that animal feed is organic or guaranteed pesticide-free.

The Real Meat Company's meat and meat products are not sold through supermarkets but through independent shops in London and Central and Southern England and by courier service.

Barn and perchery eggs

Standards for barn and perchery eggs are defined by EU regulations. Unlike battery cages, hens can in theory move about but are often so crowded that they become aggressive and fight for food and space. There is no access to the outside.

Free-range eggs

The EU's free-range egg regulations set standards which many animal welfare organisations argue are too low. There is no limit to the number of birds that can be kept in a 'free-range' chicken house and the number may commonly exceed 7,000 birds, of which only a small percentage

manage to venture outside. Even when they do go outside the area may be barren and unattractive. Campaigners would like standards that allow no more than about 300 birds in a flock, in small movable houses which allow regular fresh pasture and genuine freedom to range.

EU regulations also permit free-range birds to be exposed to extended daylight using artificial light to encourage greater egg laying but which also places unnatural stress on the birds. The practice is widespread, as is adding artificial yolk dye to colour egg yolks.

Free-range poultry

There are three sets of 'free-range' standards for poultry, 'free-range', 'traditional free-range' and 'free-range total freedom'. Only the latter provides hens with complete outdoor access – such as that enjoyed by chickens chased around French forests by Dudley Moore in Tesco adverts – but even these are permitted to be routinely fed antibiotics and other drugs.

Free-range meat

The term free-range is defined by the EU only for eggs and poultry, not for the production of other meat. A label claiming 'free-range' may be meaningless unless there are published definitions and, preferably, an independent certifying system.

Freedom Food

The RSPCA launched a certifying scheme for animal products reared according to their 'five freedoms' definitions in 1994 (see *Living Earth/ The Food Magazine*, November 1993). Both Tesco and the Co-op have adopted the RSPCA symbol on certain lines of eggs, pork and bacon and Tesco plans to extend the scheme into beef and lamb later this

year. While many of the RSPCA's standards are high compared with regular factory farming, the scheme has received criticism for failing to set standards high enough. Eggs can bear the RSPCA symbol even when they have been laid by hens that have never experienced natural light and the scheme currently permits farrowing crates, debeaking (beak tipping) of chickens, tail docking for piglets and gas stunning of pigs in slaughter houses. Live animal transport for over eight hours is banned.

Safeway

In addition to stocking organic meat in a small number of stores, Safeway have introduced a 'Heritage' range of meats including free range chicken, 'outdoor reared' pork and bacon, and traditionally matured beef and lamb. The Safeway Charter for Heritage Poultry boasts a 'cereal-based' diet and 'no herbicides or artificial fertilisers' used on the pasture on which the chickens roam. They do not say what else is allowed in feed, nor what other types of agrochemicals can be used on pasture.

Outdoor reared pork gives the impression of pigs in fields but after a 70 day period outdoors the pigs are herded together to be fattened in open barns. The pork, along with lamb 'from naturally fed flocks' and beef 'from suckler herds' is accredited by the National Farm Assurance Scheme but this only provides an audit trail, not an improvement on current livestock practices.

Sainsbury

A spokeswoman for Sainsbury says that organic pork is too difficult to obtain in commercial quantities but that its outdoor reared pork is 'just as good'. Sainsbury's outdoor reared pork is, like Safeways' pork, reared in fields and in barns, fed cereals and medicated 'for medicinal reasons only'. The company's 'Tenderlean' lamb and 'Traditional' beef are stated as grazing freely on grass in fields, with supplementary feeds in winter of silage, vegetables and cereals as are the vast majority of UK-produced beef and lamb.

Sainsbury claims that the 'difference between organic and non-organic meat is that the animals' pasture and feed is approved by UKROFS', the UK organic regulating agency. This appears to ignore the additional organic standards that UKROFS requires on animal welfare, medication, transport and slaughter procedures.

© *Living Earth & The Food Magazine*
April-June 1995

Freedom Food has arrived!

Freedom Food is a food labelling scheme devised by the RSPCA, aimed at linking the farming industry directly with consumers. It is the most exciting development in farm animal welfare for many years

It's a tough time for many livestock and dairy farmers. The food market is becoming more competitive and the industry strives to produce even cheaper food – sometimes at the expense of the conditions in which farm animals are reared.

But consumers are becoming more discerning. Most will continue to eat meat, eggs or dairy products, but they want to be sure the products are of high quality and derived from animals that have enjoyed a decent life.

Consumers also want to see clear and believable labelling which helps them to make an informed choice.

Research, commissioned recently, showed that over 80% of consumers are willing to pay more for products that meet these criteria.

Freedom Food is the answer.

What's special about Freedom Food?

There are many different products on the market claiming to offer assurances on product quality or animal welfare. But some labels can be unclear or misleading, leaving the consumer confused about how the food was produced, unconvinced that the claims are credible, or simply unaware of the differences between the range of products offered.

The RSPCA's Freedom Food label offers the consumer an independent, trusted and credible choice. Freedom Food recognises good farming practices and provides the assurance consumers now demand for quality products produced to high welfare standards.

Freedom Food is a self-funding scheme monitored by the RSPCA, the world's oldest and most respected animal welfare charity. Any surplus income from the scheme is spent on further research into farm animal welfare.

Extensive market research has confirmed that a massive 95% of consumers approve of the scheme, with 86% saying they will replace most of their current purchases with Freedom Food products when available.

How does the scheme work?

The Freedom Food labelling scheme is based on farm animal welfare standards drawn up by the RSPCA.

The standards are strict but achievable at farm level, and cover every aspect of an animal's life – from birth to slaughter.

They have been devised following consultation with specialists in all aspects of animal husbandry and are founded on the Five Freedoms which all farm animals should enjoy, supported by the Five Obligations to be fulfilled by scheme members.

Farmers, hauliers, abattoirs and all those involved in animal food production and supply are invited to become members of the scheme.

Applicants will be inspected by a team of Freedom Food specialist assessors, and monitored by the RSPCA.

Initially the scheme covers pigs and laying hens; in 1995 we look to introduce sheep and beef cattle, and eventually there will be welfare standards for all farm animals.

The Five Freedoms

These are the ideals on which the RSPCA's Freedom Food scheme is based:

1. Freedom from fear and distress
2. Freedom from pain, injury and disease
3. Freedom from hunger and thirst
4. Freedom from discomfort
5. Freedom to express normal behaviour

The Five Obligations

1. Caring and responsible management
2. Skilled, knowledgeable and conscientious stockmanship
3. Appropriate environmental design
4. Considerate handling and transport
5. Humane slaughter

What are the benefits?

- Joining the Freedom Food scheme will help producers to meet growing consumer demands for quality products made to high welfare standards, and will secure a market for the future.
- The independent endorsement provided by the RSPCA will add credibility and value to products.
- Products will be stocked in major high street outlets.
- A database will be maintained to provide lists of Freedom Food accredited hauliers, abattoirs and retail outlets, for producers' information.
- The scheme will fund research into practical, cost-effective solutions to animal welfare.
- Freedom Food is an innovative scheme that will keep Britain's farmers at the forefront of animal welfare.
- Consumers will now be able to make an informed choice.

Who will operate the scheme?

Freedom Food Ltd, a wholly owned subsidiary of the RSPCA, will operate the scheme and co-ordinate an assessment and monitoring service to ensure that members comply with all aspects of the Freedom Food standards. Freedom Food is a registered certification scheme.

© Freedom Foods Ltd

Planet on a plate

Information from Viva!

By David Gee

With every animal we kill for food, we are slowly helping to destroy our planet. While most of us know that climate change from global warming and acid rain are big problems, few realise that the meat industry contributes to these and to almost all the other serious environmental hazards that we know about.

Humans have been farming for 10,000 years but we have only kept animals in such large numbers for the last fifty. There are four times as many farm animals in the world today as there were in 1945. To support them, much of the world's tropical rainforest has been chopped down to provide grazing land, which is making global warming worse and killing off the rich variety of animals and plants that live there.

Growing food to feed animals uses vast amounts of water, reducing rivers and other water sources to dangerously low levels. Manure is polluting soils, rivers and lakes with nitrates, pesticides and growth hormones, leaving large areas without safe drinking water. Overfishing at sea is threatening all life in half of the world's main fishing areas, destroying entire marine ecosystems. As if that wasn't enough, this pursuit of animal protein consumes huge quantities of fossil fuels such as coal, oil and gas – which are themselves a source of pollution. We are creating a situation which, if it continues, can only bring the planet to its knees.

Meat the consumer

The world gorged its way through 170 million metric tonnes of meat in 1990 – and the figure is rising as factory farming becomes popular in poorer countries.

Fossil fuels are used at every stage of meat production – growing fodder, building factory farms, fattening and transporting animals and refrigerating the carcasses.

Animals waste most of the energy from the food they eat, consequently almost 800kg of plant protein is needed to produce just 50kg of beef. To produce salmon requires 40 times the amount of energy that it gives as food value, lobster almost 200. Considering everything we eat, it takes twice as much energy to produce food for a meat and fish-based diet than for a vegetarian diet and four times as much than for a vegan diet (which excludes dairy products and eggs).

There are now three times as many farm animals (livestock) in the world as people. It is almost unbelievable that over 1,000 million people live in hunger while livestock munch their way through 38 per cent of all grain grown in the world – 90 per cent of its nutrients simply being converted to manure.

Land use

Animals use large amounts of land, both for grazing and growing feed crops. In tropical areas, rainforests are being ripped up and replaced with a single crop: grass. In cooler areas like Europe, farmers try to squeeze everything from their land by using fertilisers and pesticides, which work for a short time but eventually pollute the environment and destroy the structure of the soil.

Farms in Britain have become bigger and bigger to help satisfy the demand for meat. Just six per cent of farms grow most of our cereals (e.g. wheat) and take up half of all agricultural land. Fifty per cent of grain is then fed to farm animals.

Changing to a vegetarian diet would have a dramatic effect. Land that supports only two people with meat could then support up to 60 on a plant-based diet. Those with a vested interest in meat, while not denying these figures, claim they don't matter as cows graze on otherwise useless land. Don't believe it – the mixture of fields growing crops and animals grazing side by side is there for all to see.

It is the hyped up demands on the land for animal feed (three-quarters of all agricultural land in the UK is used for livestock), along with warped government policies which are largely responsible for

stark, prairie-like monocultures; for the destruction of 109,000 miles of hedgerow; for excessive use of nitrates and pesticides; and for the huge quantities of polluting liquid dung.

Remove meat and you remove the need to force-feed the land – chemical fertilisers cannot indefinitely mask the decline in top soil fertility and its erosion. The more people that go vegetarian and vegan, the more we can allow the land to breathe again, to grow food at a sustainable rate. We take pressure off disappearing habitats and allow new ones to flourish.

Global warming

The earth's climate has warmed between 0.3 and 0.6 degrees centigrade in the last century and the five hottest years on record have all been in the 1980s and 1990s. The burning of fossil fuels and the clearance of land for agriculture are the two main causes.

Animals, both directly and indirectly, play a big part in warming the atmosphere with three major greenhouse gases – methane, carbon dioxide and nitrous oxides. Deforestation is responsible for 20 per cent of all the carbon dioxide released into the atmosphere, largely from burning the undergrowth.

This is the most well-known greenhouse gas but methane is 25 times more effective in trapping heat. It also helps to destroy the ozone layer by releasing water-forming hydrogen as it breaks down in the stratosphere. Clouds of frozen water in this normally dry environment contribute to the destruction of the ozone layer.

A cow belches or farts out 200 litres of methane a day from its digestive processes. Multiply that by the world's 1.3 billion cattle and the total is 100 million tonnes every year, a massive 20 per cent of the total output of methane. Animal manure gives off another 35 million tonnes.

Farm animals produce 26 per cent of the total UK methane emissions. By the year 2025, a 40-60 per cent increase in methane emissions from animals worldwide is predicted, plus a 30-40 per cent increase from animal manure, if we carry on as we are.

Nitrous oxide is another ozone eater. It disintegrates extremely slowly, staying in the atmosphere for 150 years, long enough to be transported up to the higher strato-sphere where it reacts with ozone, destroying it. The large-scale use of fertilisers and burning of coal, oil and gas are responsible for 45 per cent of nitrous oxide. Of all the greenhouse gases, this is one of the most potent. The index of Global Warming Potential (GWP) rates each gas with points, according to how much it contributes to global warming. For carbon dioxide the GWP is 1, methane 11 and nitrous oxide 270.

Rainforests

So much rainforest is being ripped up around the globe that if it continues, little or none will be left by the year 2030. Worldwide, deforestation is responsible for around 30 per cent of all greenhouse gases – chopping down the Amazon rainforest alone was responsible for 9 per cent of all global warming in 1987. In Latin America, most forests are cut down to clear land so cattle can graze on it.

As well as causing global warming, the destruction of rainforests wipes out plants, animals and people. With them, an enormous and largely undiscovered store of valuable information and resources is lost. Quinine, the drug used to prevent malaria, was discovered from a tribal treatment for acute fever and extracts from rainforest plants have been developed for use in modern medicine for treating illnesses such as multiple sclerosis and Parkinson's Disease.

Of the 3,000 plants that we know have anti-cancer properties, 70 per cent have come from the rainforests. When we consider that they may contain a future cure for diseases such as AIDS, is the rainforest really worth more dead than alive?

Most scientists now think that our natural ecosystems can only cope with a rise in temperature of one or two degrees before they are seriously damaged. Simply to keep the amount of greenhouse gases in the atmosphere at today's levels, we would need to reduce emissions by 50 to 80 per cent. One environmental group, Earthsave, has worked out that eating a steak warms the earth as much as a 25-mile drive in a typical American car.

Soils and desertification

All the world's food comes from the ground, grown in the highly fertile upper layer of soil known as topsoil. This topsoil is essential to life. If it becomes 'exhausted' because of over use, crop harvests begin to fall. Eventually, it becomes dusty and lifeless and can be lost altogether – simply washed or blown away. Bad farming practices like this were responsible for the disappearance of several past civilisations.

Farms in the US are losing 5000 million tonnes of soil every year. Most of it (85 per cent) from cropland, pasture, rangeland and forest is because of livestock agriculture. Over half of all US cropland is used to feed livestock. Because today people eat more meat, we need to grow more crops; to grow more crops, we use

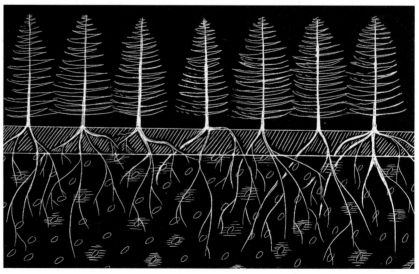

more fertiliser; more fertiliser erodes the soil. This has caused desertification in some arid lands and is causing problems in the developed world as well.

Another main cause of soil erosion is deforestation for cattle ranching. The forest's thick cover of vegetation and ground litter absorbs rainfall and prevents flooding. When these are removed, animals trample and compress the soil, eat tree seedlings and strip bark from mature trees. The land is left completely open with no protection so soil is baked hard by the sun and washed away by the rains.

In England and Wales, 44 per cent of soil used to grow crops is in danger of being eroded because of modern farming methods. Increasingly, large, heavy machinery is used which squashes soil and damages its structure. Also, some crop seeds are now planted in autumn instead of spring so the soil is left vulnerable and exposed to wind and rain over the winter.

Hedgerow removal also causes problems, taking away natural wind breaks. Overgrazing by sheep in upland areas such as the Peak District and the Clwyd Ranges in Wales has also caused soil erosion.

The eventual outcome is that once fertile areas turn into desert and this is happening more and more on every continent. The process can be made quicker by changes in the climate but the main causes are overcultivation, overgrazing, deforestation and poor irrigation. The United Nations Food & Agriculture Organisation blames these causes for 80 per cent of worldwide desertification.

● The above is an extract from *Planet on a plate*, guide number 9 by David Gee, published by Viva! See page 39 for address details.

© Viva!

Feeding the world

From the Meat and Livestock Commission

Mankind is an omnivore, and all the available archaeological evidence suggests this has been the case for 4-5 million years. So meat has always been part of our diet, although there have been, and continue to be, variations in the meat/vegetable material ratio – depending on considerations such as availability, wealth, race and religion. Moral concerns are matters for individuals.

The Meat and Livestock Commission respects the right of individuals to choose not to eat meat but believes the vast majority who choose to do so should certainly not feel or be made to feel guilty.

Eating less meat in the UK will not make more grain available for starvation relief overseas. The amount of grain used for meat production in the UK is less than one-third of the supplies available after domestic human needs have been met. Eating meat does not deprive the Third World of food or contribute directly to ecological problems. Refraining from eating meat has no effect on alleviating the situation.

On a global scale there is a surplus of grain. In 1989/90 world stocks of grain totalled 300 million tonnes, 44 per cent of which was held in developing countries. This surplus has little to do with the meat industry and illustrates that the problem of hunger lies in poverty, not availability, and the cost of transferring the surplus grain.

The solution in most cases is not agricultural, but political. Moreover, Third World countries like Botswana earn vital foreign currency for their sales of meat to Western countries to help develop their economies. British produced meat (and EC production) cannot be associated with rainforest destruction and neither can the overwhelming amount of imported meat (New Zealand lamb, Danish and Dutch bacon).

Natural recycling of waste is sensible in that it feeds back nutrients

> *The problem of hunger lies in poverty not availability, and the cost of transferring the surplus grain*

and helps condition the soil but this must be managed effectively to stop run-off and down-river pollution. Obviously, this is an area which concerns many other industries, both within and outside the food chain.

In environmental terms, increased fertiliser usage could be expected if grassland in the UK were converted to cereal or vegetable production. One point often made by the Vegetarian Society is that if land and grain were not used for meat production the Third World could be supplied with the surplus arable production that resulted.

This is manifest nonsense – 75 per cent of British agricultural land is not suitable for arable production (e.g. moorland and rough pasture). The only crop grown in such areas is grass – not noted for its food value to humans.

Additionally, Britain already exports 2 per cent of the grain it produces. Another popular misconception is the destruction of rainforests to produce beef. Imports of beef into Britain from Third World countries are minuscule.

© The Meat and Livestock Commission
June, 1995

Meat – the facts

Information from the Meat and Livestock Commission (MLC)

Food safety

In the past 10 years consumers have become increasingly aware of what they eat and its quality. Meat is no exception and the meat industry, from farm to retail, has developed to meet this demand.

The meat industry is well aware that the consumer is king and has developed its quality assurance schemes with this in mind. If meat wasn't healthy, wholesome and safe, it would not sell. The industry cannot afford not to be the best.

British produced meat does not contain added hormones. British produced meat does not contain harmful chemicals.

Occasionally toxins, such as pesticides and traces of heavy metals, may be found in meat and come from the feeds which the animals eat. These same substances will also occasionally be found in and on cereals and vegetables which humans eat.

The Government's National Surveillance Monitoring Scheme regularly checks meat and offal in order to ensure that levels are kept to an acceptable minute minimum.

The British food industry and in particular the meat industry is one of the most controlled and highly regulated industries in Europe. A total of over 50 separate pieces of legislation cover all aspects of meat safety from production through to retail sale and the statutory and voluntary controls have never been tighter.

British meat safety controls are second to none anywhere and are much more strictly applied than in most other countries.

In addition, MLC operates an increasing number of quality assurance schemes from farm to retail which are even more stringent than all EC and UK legislation.

Standards of hygiene in abattoirs are monitored by Environmental Health Officers, Authorised Meat Inspectors and Official Veterinary Surgeons. This system extends both to animals prior to slaughter and meat on the production line. There are strictly laid down requirements in both UK and EC law for abattoirs.

Regulations for hygiene control in British abattoirs include:
- Slaughterhouses (Hygiene) Regulations 1977
- The Food (Meat Inspection) Regulations 1987
- The Fresh Meat Export (Hygiene & Inspection) Regulations 1987
- Food Hygiene (General) Regulations 1970

The main authority responsible for their implementation is the Ministry of Agriculture, Fisheries and Food.

Listeria is a very common organism in our environment and has been found in all types of cook-chill meals and is not related to whether they contain meat or not. It has also been found in ready-to-eat poultry, soft cheeses, ready prepared salads and pâtés (including meatless pâté).

For this reason, to be on the safe side, pregnant women are advised by the Department of Health to reheat all cook-chill foods thoroughly until they are piping hot and not to eat any type of pâté, including fish.

Campylobacter is another organism which is very common throughout the environment, and it can cause abortion in sheep and cattle. Two of its sub-species are associated with food poisoning and entercolitis in man, being present in the human gut, and the gut of farm animals, pets, poultry and wildlife. Campylobacter has been detected in most foods – including poultry and even in water!

© Meat and Livestock Commission

The meat industry is one of the most controlled and highly regulated industries in Europe

Getting to the meat of the matter

Vegetarian Society Chair of Council, Maxwell Lee, explores the philosophical and moral background to a vegetarian diet

I t is often claimed, especially by certain religious groups, that animals were put on Earth for people to use as they think fit. This point of view helps explain the extent of human misuse of the animal kingdom. The attitude to animals among many people is rather similar to that adopted by *superior* beings towards those considered of lesser value. Slavery, for long an established and accepted way of treating others in human societies, reflects an attitude which is similar to that adopted towards animals by many people in contemporary society. Respect for life is a slogan often quoted today and one should reflect on it and its importance in suggesting respect not only for other humans but also for all life forms whether animal or vegetable. All have their place in the world. We need to live on something and it is often suggested we should go as far down the food chain as possible for our food. Vegetarians have gone part of the way and vegans and fruitarians even further. These three valid approaches are based on respect for life and the view that animals should be treated much better by humans.

Cruelty is virtually endemic in human society and one can but wonder what it is that makes so many humans seek and enjoy cruelty in their lives. The cruelties in so-called sports are worthy of considerable attention in their own right. However, this article is mainly concerned with the vegetarian approach. Some do not consider it cruel to eat animals and suggest that they are well treated whilst they are alive. Of course, this has become patently untrue with the growth of factory farming methods and the lack of any consideration for natural behaviour in animals. Whether it is

putting calves into boxes which deny them access to their mothers, the open air and the green fields which are their natural habitat, or keeping chickens in intensive systems which deny them the ability to spread their wings and carry out their natural habits; these and many other practices are all based on a lack of concern and care for the animals.

The arguments quoted in their favour are economic although those who practise such cruelties usually suggest the animals prefer such treatment. If such practices are not cruel, what are they? Suggesting as some do that animals do not choose to come out of sheds and similar conditions even if the doors are left open is more the result of conditioning than choice. One thing is sure, the animals are not given that choice! Modern Western society has much to answer for in encouraging a meat/animal based diet. Unfortunately, some in the developing world see such an approach as Western and this means attractive! They give scant regard to the

---

Farmers like to pump the waste into water courses, streams and rivers to pollute and destroy the eco-systems which have existed for so long

---

treatment of the animals and the effects of meat eating on health and the environment. Population pressure in many developing countries is argument enough for cutting down and abandoning a meat based diet.

Animal production in intensive systems concentrates the animal waste products rather than spreading them over the fields as manure for the future. What was once seen as desirable now becomes a nuisance and an economic problem. Disposal of the waste is costly and the problem is closely related to the increase in meat consumption. Farmers like to pump the waste into water courses, streams and rivers to pollute and destroy the eco-systems which have existed for so long. In addition, the intensive nature of factory farming means disease is much more likely to spread so animals are treated with large amounts of antibiotics, growth enhancers and similar products. Of course, these concentrate in the meat and lead to illnesses and disease in humans. Additionally, some of them find their way into the water system and are taken up further along the water course where the impure water is once again pumped out for human use and purification does not remove all these residues.

The rise of cancer, heart disease, kidney and liver disease, as well as diabetes and a variety of other health conditions, relates closely to the increase in meat consumption. Medical research provides ample evidence that a vegetarian diet is better for health and that the incidence of many unpleasant diseases is much less common among vegetarians. It is good to do something for moral reasons but even better when one discovers that it is good for one's health as well!

The growth of vegetarianism in the Western world is testament to the increasing desire among many people to live a more humane, healthy and environmentally friendly way of life. In North America, South America, Europe and Australasia there is a marked and continuing growth of vegetarianism. In Eastern Europe and Middle Europe since the political changes, there has been an upsurge in interest in vegetarianism. Vegetarian and animal movements have been developed and are winning increasing support. In Asia, governmental encouragement to meat consumption is being resisted by vegetarian groups. In a country like India with a long history of Ahimsa, respect for life and so vegetarianism, the battle for vegetarianism is being waged by religious and moral groups as well as environmentalists and doctors who appreciate the benefits of the vegetarian approach. In Britain the surge to vegetarianism has been very marked in the last twenty years so that now vegetarians are no longer seen as strange or odd but part of the mainstream. Vegetarian meals are available in all parts of the country and young people are moving towards vegetarianism. Supermarkets display a good range of vegetarian products, making shopping much easier and drawing the attention of meat-eaters to the wide variety of good healthy and humane foods which vegetarians eat. Linda McCartney, who together with her husband Paul recently became Patrons of The Vegetarian Society of the United Kingdom, has produced a range of imitation meat products including pies and sausages which are attracting many people who do not consider themselves vegetarian. Such developments are increasingly being mirrored in other countries.

Modern technology has a great deal to answer for in relation to human treatment of animals. Recently, the rise in biotechnology and genetic engineering has led to new ways of using animals for human purposes and morality seems to be little considered when thinking of the ways in which species can be engineered to enable humans to exploit them more fully. If humans have rights over animals it can equally be argued they have responsibilities. This means they need to consider the animal, its welfare and its good. Unfortunately, the present situation suggests these issues are given little if any attention by the vast majority of people. The only issue which concerns them is maximising the economic return from the animals.

Often it is argued that because animals are different species from humans, the way in which we treat them is not important. Of course, people who express such views might equally not be too concerned about how other human societies are treated. Many of us can see a relationship between the two. People who treat other humans with respect are more likely to show respect to other species. More than once one has heard the suggestion that concern for animals should be replaced by concern for humans. People interested in animal rights are normally just as concerned about human suffering. We know that animals feel pain and suffer and show distress. We cannot fully understand their thought processes but there is ample evidence that animals have their societies and their way of life.

Who is to say that in the fullness of time their rights should be any less than those expected and sought by humans? Many animals are less intelligent than humans but there is considerable variation in intelligence among humans. If one argues that the lower intelligence of many animals gives us the right to treat them as we will, without real concern, then one might equally argue that less intelligent humans might be similarly treated. Indeed, certain political philosophies, although very much discredited, have put forward such arguments. We are on this planet for a finite time and how we interact and use the planet will affect future generations, possibly until the end of the world as we know it. One can claim that it is in our interest to minimise suffering and malpractice that animals and humans suffer, and to move to a more humane world at peace with itself. Assuming that this is a goal that the vast majority of people see as desirable then we need to improve our treatment of both humans and animals. People generally wish to live a healthy life and the vegetarian approach is one that leads in that direction while also minimising the suffering of other animal species. The whole meat-eating approach is based on hypocrisy. People use some animals as pets and treat them in a special way. Other animals are often seen as pests or food so they do not warrant the care and protection that pets receive. It is worth remembering that, in many countries, if one were to treat one's pet animals in the way in which farm animals are treated, then one would be liable to prosecution in the courts. Many wild animals receive no legal protection at all and are therefore hunted and anyone else can seek them out and treat them as they wish.

It is my contention that the future of the world is very much related to how we treat our weaker fellow creatures. Cruelty and evil should play no part in a civilised society. Although we often claim that we are civilised I would contend that this is far from the case. These days we look upon slavery with horror and find it hard to understand how such practices have lasted for so long and even now exist in some parts of the world. As we move away from human slavery we need to look to the next step and move away from animal slavery. Both for moral and selfish reasons a vegetarian world lacking exploitation and cruelty to humans and other animals needs to be our goal. If we do not bother now, the future of all creatures will continue to be bleak.

© *The Vegetarian Society*

> *It is my contention that the future of the world is very much related to how we treat our weaker fellow creatures. Cruelty and evil should play no part in a civilised society*

So you want to be a vegetarian?

Around 2000 people a week decide to go veggie – but does a meat-free diet make you any healthier, and is it really worth the effort?

Although the main reason for going vegetarian is concern for animal welfare, the quest for a healthier diet has made many people feel they'd be better off without meat. But are vegetarians any healthier than the rest of us? Just giving up meat doesn't make your diet any better – in fact, it could mean you're missing out on essential nutrients, especially iron, and protein – needed for the growth and repair of the body's cells. Dropping meat and not replacing it with the right type of vegetable protein can leave you in worse, not better health. On the other hand, a well-balanced vegetarian diet does offer important benefits – studies show that vegetarians are less likely to get both heart disease and cancer. To get the picture straight, we asked Lyndel Costain of The British Dietetic Association to analyse three vegetarian readers' diets.

Hannah Bunzle, 19, is working as a waitress and a primary school assistant during her year off before starting college.
'I've been vegetarian since my first year at secondary school,' says Hannah. 'My family went vegetarian for a month, after which my mum, dad and brother all went back to eating meat. I decided to stay vegetarian because I didn't fancy the idea of killing animals.

'I get up late, so I don't have time for breakfast, just a drink of orange squash. Lunch depends on where I am. At school, the choice is an egg or cheese salad with lettuce and tomato, a baked potato with grated cheese, or a white cheese roll with a packet of crisps and an apple. When I'm at the restaurant my only option is a bowl of soup.

'At home in the evening, I have pasta with a mushroom sauce or maybe fried rice with vegetables, such as leeks, onion or peppers. For a special-occasion meal, I'll make a vegetarian lasagna with soya bolognese and cheesy white sauce layers. I normally drink water or orange squash during the day, or hot chocolate made with milk, and I hardly ever have alcohol.'

Lyndel comments . . .
'Hannah's diet is quite restricted and I'm concerned she's not getting enough vegetable protein. She may also be short on iron and vitamins. Hannah should eat breakfast regularly and swap her white roll for wholemeal bread – it contains more iron, zinc and B vitamins. And, as a drink, fruit juice is better then squash. Finally, Hannah needs to add protein

in the form of beans, lentils, Quorn, nuts, eggs or soya meat to her evening meal, and should eat one or two pieces of fruit a day.'

Joanne Taylor, 25, is a trainee pharmacist's dispensary technician; her husband Alan, 26, is a stonemason. Their daughter Lisle is three.
'I became a vegetarian seven years ago after reading an article about factory farming,' says Joanne. 'Alan used to eat meat at work, but now he's decided he doesn't really need it.

'It's quite hard work bringing up a vegetarian child, but I had a lot of help from my health visitor. We all have cereal and milk in the morning and, at lunch, Alan has brown bread with cheese and tomato or egg sandwiches, and crisps bought at work. Lisle and I tend to have

Ken Pyne

wholemeal sandwiches with cheese or mock-chicken or ham vegetable protein slices.

'At night, we have Quorn casserole, or a hotpot; spaghetti bolognese, curry or chilli made with soya mince, or vegetable protein, served with another vegetable, such as broccoli, parsnips or carrots. During the summer, we have salads with quiches, and for pudding we eat apple or rhubarb crumble with cream or ice cream. Also, I often have a milk shake with my pudding, or an all-milk coffee.'

Lyndel comments. . .
'Joanne is generally doing well, with a good vegetarian diet for her family, but she could be overdoing the dairy produce a bit. She drinks a lot of milk and should change to a lower-fat variety, and have custard, not cream, with her puddings. Lisle and Alan can still have full-cream milk; they need extra calories – Lisle because she's growing and Alan because of his physically demanding job.'

Rachel McKernan, 20, is an administrator for a south London national health trust.
'I'm a demi-vegetarian and have always eaten this way. I try to eat healthily, but I worry about snacking on too much chocolate, nuts and crisps. I try not to eat too much sugar as it gives me spots,' says Rachel.

'For breakfast, I have no sugar or low-sugar muesli with nuts, seeds, dried fruits and live natural yogurt, with a fresh apple or banana sliced on top. Then I may have wholemeal stoneground toast with some sun-flower spread and no-added-sugar jam or peanut butter and a cup of herb tea. At around 11am, I have fruit, nuts or crisps. Lunch is a home-made cheese and salad or peanut butter sandwich with fruit or nuts and maybe a yogurt.

'If I'm at home, I have a vegetable quiche and salad, soup and a roll or cheese on toast. In the afternoon, I have fruit, nuts or crisps and often a bar of chocolate. At home in the evening I have a jacket potato, salad and vegetable quiche, or a vegetable stew.

'Once a week, I eat either grilled

fish or grilled chicken breast with potatoes or boiled brown rice or lentils and vegetables. Also, once every two months or so I eat lamb or duck. I never have fizzy drinks, tea or coffee, and I have a couple of glasses of white wine a week.'

Lyndel comments. . .
'Rachel should try to get extra calories from eating more at meals, then she might not need to eat so many smaller snacks. While nuts are nutritious, they are also high in fat, so cut down to no more than 25g/1oz a day; crisps are quite high in fat, too. Rachel should aim for two to three pieces of fruit a day to replace the crisps and chocolate. Her evening meal should contain a meat alter-native, such as beans, eggs, soya protein, Quorn or lentils. But her diet is generally well balanced, containing meat alternatives, starchy foods and dairy foods, and includes fruit and vegetables, too.'

Your questions answered
Q. As a strict vegetarian, am I missing out on essential fatty acids that are found in fish and fish oils?
A. Non-vegetarians should eat fish twice a week. This is because fish reduces the risk of heart disease due to high levels of EPA (eicosapen-taenoic acid) – an omega-3 fatty acid. Vegetarians shouldn't worry, though, as they can get the essential fatty acid, alphalinolenic acid, from soya and rapeseed oils, pulses, walnuts and green leafy vegetables, which is then converted in the body to EPA. The second type of essential fatty acid is linoleic acid (omega-6 fatty acid) and comes in sunflower oil,

vegetables, fruit, nuts and cereals, all of which are well supplied in a good vegetarian diet.

Q. Does a vegetarian diet give you wind?
A. Switching to a good vegetarian diet means eating more pulses, wholemeal bread, pasta, brown rice and other high-fibre foods, which can cause wind. Some people are more susceptible than others, but the problem usually subsides as the naturally occurring bacteria in the gut adjust to the changes. You could try eating more live yogurt to speed up the adjustment.

Q. Is eating vegetarian food more expensive?
A. It needn't be. Many vegetarians say it's a lot cheaper as they eat more pasta, rice, beans, pulses, bread and vegetables, which generally cost less. Seasonal fruit is inexpensive, as are frozen vegetables, which are as beneficial as fresh. Dairy foods and vegetarian protein foods, such as Quorn, soya proteins and tofu are cheaper than lean, humanely farmed meats. A vegetarian diet not only costs less, but it helps the earth's resources go further as it's cheaper and more environmentally friendly to produce vegetable crops.

Five steps to a healthy diet
These quick guidelines will help to make sure you're getting your diet right:
- Eat most of your food from starchy complex carbohydrates (cereals and grains), such as bread, pasta, rice and potatoes.
- Eat at least five servings of fruit or vegetables every day, including dark green leafy vegetables and red, orange and yellow fruit and vegetables.
- Eat a couple of moderate servings of protein foods daily – the vegetarian products to look out for are pulses, nuts or seeds, dairy or soya foods.
- Eat small amounts of butter, margarine or vegetable oils.
- Limit your intake of fatty and sugary foods – biscuits, cakes, ice cream, mayonnaise, pies, and so on – to only one helping a day.
© Essentials
April, 1996

What the experts say

From the Meat and Livestock Commission

Man is an omnivore and all the available archaeological evidence suggests this was the case for his predecessors. Meat has always been part of our diet, although there have been, and continue to be, variations in the ratio to vegetable material, depending on such considerations as availability, wealth, race and religion.

The suitability of an omnivorous diet is borne out by our dentition and digestive system. Added credibility is given to the argument by man's determined efforts over many centuries to harness and develop the technologies of agriculture and meat production and in more recent times by the general move towards increased meat consumption in those countries whose economies are developing.

Essentially, it comes down to a question of choice. About 97 per cent of consumers in Britain choose to buy and consume meat on a regular or an occasional basis. They do this for a variety of reasons: they like its taste, they believe it to be nutritious, it is versatile, consumers find it satisfying. Meat purchases represent nearly a quarter of household expenditure on food.

In short, reasonable-minded consumers in our society feel they can afford in cash and moral terms to exercise choice in their diet, with no damage to collective health, to their consciences or, indeed, to the Third World or the earth's atmosphere. These are among the major issues aired by the anti-meat-eating lobby in pursuit of their aims and should therefore be examined further.

Some vegetarians claim they are more healthy than the general population. But vegetarianism, almost by definition, requires a stricter attention to total diet to achieve balance. Because of the interest in their diets of this relatively small proportion of the population and because of the generally higher level of motivation vegetarians tend to pursue a healthier lifestyle.

They certainly consume less alcohol and the other nasties like nicotine.

The remaining 97 per cent of the population are bound to contain a significantly higher number of people who are more relaxed about their lifestyles. They may tend to be more self-indulgent with a few more 'blow-outs and binges', with less exercise and more smoking, drinking and consumption of greasy or junk foods.

Meat is not only a good source of iron, but the iron absorption from meat is at least twice as great as from plant foods

---

However, there will also be quite a few budding Seb Coes or Liz McColgans in this sector, those who take regular exercise, watch their diet – with lean meat playing an important part – and who are fit and healthy.

Studies done on Seventh Day Adventists, who follow a vegetarian diet, show they have a lower incidence of cancer and heart disease. But vegetarianism is only part of the equation as this sector of society does not smoke, drink tea, coffee or alcohol.

Meat eating is not an unhealthy activity. It must be remembered meat eaters are not carnivores but omnivores – meat and meat products provide about 15 per cent of their total energy intake and they consume a large amount of fruit, vegetables and cereals.

Meat is not only a good source of iron, but the iron absorption from meat is at least twice as great as from plant foods. In addition, meat enhances the absorption of iron from cereals and vegetables.

This is particularly important in view of the 1990 Department of Health finding that three per cent of women in Britain have low haemoglobin levels and 42 per cent of those aged between 18 and 49 have low iron stores.

Meat is an important source of unsaturated fatty acids, both mono-unsaturated and poly-unsaturated. Only half the fat is saturated. It is important to point out that, trimmed of the visible fat round the edges, all red meats are much lower in fat than is often portrayed.

Britain has the highest rate of heart disease among EC countries but the second lowest meat consumption per person – just ahead of Portugal. France, on the other hand, has the highest meat consumption and the lowest heart disease rate.

The argument that meat eating by developed countries disadvantages Third World nations is unfounded. It tends to be based on the precept that it takes 10 tonnes of grain to produce one tonne of beef. In Britain, and most of northern Europe, the base for much of meat production is grassland; grain and concentrate feeds are used as supplements for some ruminants and as the main feed for pigs and poultry.

The efficiency of cereals is such that only just over a third of that produced in this country is used to satisfy animal feed demand, with slightly less going to human use, leaving a further third, approximately, for export or buffer stocks. Whether these reserves should go for food aid is a totally separate argument.

Critics of meat eating have tried to exploit the public's heightened awareness of these global problems by suggesting that giving up meat eating in this country will alleviate hunger elsewhere.

How, then, do we raise livestock in this country and does this consume resources that could otherwise be used to feed starving and hungry people?

Much of the grassland in the UK is not usable for the production of crops and so livestock production presents the best and, in many cases, only alternative. The total agricultural area of the UK is just over 18 million hectares of which nearly 13 million hectares is grassland.

Of this, almost half is classified as 'rough grazing' and so is suitable only for livestock or forestation. A further 40 per cent is 'permanent pasture' and as such can only be converted to crops after considerable investment to improve the quality of the land sufficiently.

It is superficially tempting to believe the 9.6 million tonnes of grain fed to animals in this country could somehow be easily transported to feed the hungry in developing countries. With the exception of emergency food aid, the shipment of large volumes of food causes severe problems in developing nations: it reduces market prices, stifles local agriculture and leaves developing countries dangerously dependent on donor governments.

A considerable amount of otherwise waste food materials is incorporated in manufactured compound feeds making animals efficient recyclers – for example, maize gluten (left after the production of cornflakes) and citrus pulp (after extraction of fruit juices).

The solution to alleviating world hunger lies in the disappearance of global poverty. This is a complex political, social and economic problem of truly global proportions and it needs to be tackled on several fronts. To offer the 'simple' solution that eating less meat will in some way help is unfounded.

Many experts believe agriculture must move towards systems

> *It is superficially tempting to believe the 9.6 million tonnes of grain fed to animals in this country could somehow be easily transported to feed the hungry in developing countries*

using fewer resources and causing less environmental damage – but sustainable agriculture world-wide must involve a sensible balance of animal and plant production. Mixed farming systems can achieve yields and maintain soil fertility without high chemical inputs.

Grass breaks allow livestock to graze in summer and provide food for their over-wintering with minimum supplementation, and feed back organic material to the soil. Monocultures, involving continuous cropping and high nitrogen use or continuous grazing, can lead to soil starvation and erosion.

Methane emissions from ruminants have been calculated to make a four per cent contribution to the greenhouse effect, but scientists worldwide accept the major man-made emissions (CO_2 from fossil fuel burning and methane from landfill and rice paddies) are higher priorities for urgent action.

Some opponents of livestock production have suggested that so-called 'factory farming' is widespread and cruel. Firstly, it has to be emphasised that beef cattle and sheep are essentially reared out-of-doors, although cattle are mostly housed in the winter when weather and grass growth dictates.

Secondly, less than half the national pig herd is reared intensively. Most are reared in loose housing conditions, with an increasing number of outdoor herds. Stalls and tethers are being phased out.

A final argument against meat eating is that the slaughter of animals is barbaric. For some, this is a protest against the conditions of slaughter – for others simply a blanket condemnation on principle.

Slaughtering, it must be emphasised, is a carefully controlled procedure and conducted in the most humane manner possible in the light of current knowledge.

● The above article is from an information pack, *What the experts say*; published by the Meat and Livestock Commission. See page 39 for address details.

© *Meat and Livestock Commission*
June, 1996

Beef cattle and sheep are essentially reared out-of-doors, although cattle are mostly housed in the winter when weather and grass growth dictates

Why go vegetarian?

Vegetarians are very much like everyone else. They eat many of the same things as meat-eaters, shop in the same supermarkets (but spend less time in certain meaty aisles!), and even eat out in many of the same places.

There was a time when being a vegetarian was seen as being quite weird, but the facts speak for themselves.

What's so strange about wanting to eat healthy, fresh food that hasn't died for the dinner table? Vegetarianism is good for the environment and doesn't cost the earth.

Factory farming

Story books show farms as cosy places where hens run around in the yard, pigs wallow in mud and lambs play in the fields. Unfortunately, reality isn't always like that. Most modern farms are more like factories and the animals are treated like food-producing machines.

Many animals are kept shut up in crowded sheds their whole life through. Some will have been changed by selective breeding and genetic engineering so that they grow faster, have more offspring, grow more wool or produce more milk than any animal would in the wild.

These changes don't benefit the animals – they just increase profits. Factory farms also deny animals their natural instincts. They cannot move around freely, care for their young or even choose their food.

Just imagine being locked in the school toilets with 30 or 40 other people for the rest of your life, with nothing to do – no television, games, or music and only porridge to eat.

Broiler brutality

There is no scratching around the farmyard for chickens on modern factory farms. Known as broilers, up to 100,000 birds are kept together in windowless sheds with dim electric lights. They are fed on a high protein diet and given antibiotics to help them grow faster so that by the time they are six or seven weeks old, the chickens are twice as heavy as they should be. This excess weight causes problems such as lameness, arthritis and even leg deformities.

The sheds are never cleaned out during the life of the chickens – the layer of droppings just gets higher and higher. Lots of birds die from disease and stress and rot where they fall.

At six or seven weeks old, the birds are rounded up and stuffed into crates. Some get their wings or legs broken at this stage. The crates are loaded onto lorries and driven to the slaughterhouse.

Assault and battery

Ninety per cent of the eggs you find in shops are laid by hens kept in battery cages. These wire cages usually house five birds and are so small that each bird has just about the same amount of space as this page. They can't stretch their wings, make a nest or take a dust bath and their feet become deformed from standing on the wire mesh all the time. Many have almost all their feathers plucked out by bored or aggressive cage mates. Some birds have their beaks sliced off with a hot wire or blade to stop this feather

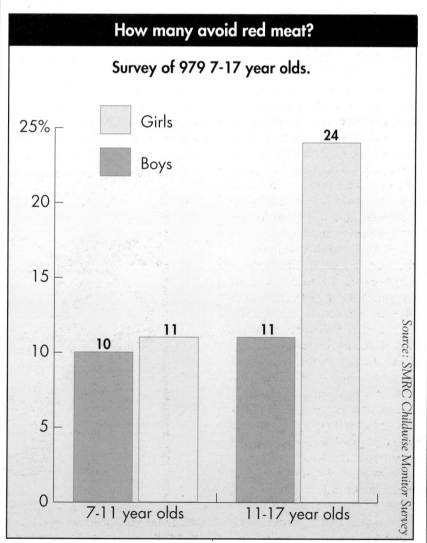

How many avoid red meat?

Survey of 979 7-17 year olds.

Girls

Boys

25%

20

15

10 — (10) (11) (11) 24

5

0

7-11 year olds   11-17 year olds

Source: SMRC Childwise Monitor Survey

plucking. Wild hens would live for 12 years, but battery hens are worn out by the time they are two and sent for slaughter.

The pork on your fork

Pigs are as intelligent and sensitive as dogs, but most are sentenced to a life of boredom and misery. Wild pigs live in woodland areas and the sows like to build a nest of grass and leaves for their young. In factory farms they have to give birth in a narrow metal crate, where they can't turn round and can only move one step backwards or forwards.

The piglets are taken away from their mother when they are only three to four weeks old so the sow can be mated again. They are fattened up in overcrowded pens, and killed at five to seven months old to become pork, bacon and ham.

Luckless lambs

You can still see lambs skipping around in fields and so most people think that sheep don't have too bad a time. They don't realise what goes on behind the scenes. For example, four million lambs die every year within a few days of being born. Often the pregnant ewes are not fed well, or they are forced to have their lambs earlier in the year than would happen naturally. As the farmers try to save money, fewer shepherds now have to look after bigger and bigger flocks, and many lambs die of exposure on cold, lonely hilltops.

Beyond beef

There are different breeds of cows – some are kept for beef and some for milk.

A dairy cow must have a calf every year, otherwise her milk dries up. Her calf is usually taken away after only a few days, so that we can drink its milk. More calves are born than are needed in a dairy herd, so the unwanted ones are sent to livestock markets. Some will be fattened up as beef, but around 500,000 a year are sent overseas to veal crates which are banned in this country because they are so cruel.

Cows would naturally live for about 20 years, but are worn out after six or seven years in dairy herds and are slaughtered.

Pigs are as intelligent and sensitive as dogs, but most are sentenced to a life of boredom and misery

Killing with kindness?

Lots of people think that it's acceptable to eat meat because they have been told that animals in this country are killed humanely. A pistol with a 15cm bolt is shot into the brain to stun the animal so that it feels no pain when its throat is being cut.

But the bolt has to hit the right spot exactly. If the animal moves its head as the pistol is fired, it could end up painfully wounded but fully conscious. One RSPCA report showed that up to half of all young bulls may suffer terrible pain as the stun gun fails to hit the target.

Smaller animals are stunned with electric shocks, and poultry are dunked head first into an electrically charged water bath. Many birds don't hang meekly on the conveyor belt, but move around trying to escape. Some move at the wrong time, missing both the stunning bath and the knife. They end up being plunged alive into a scalding tank designed to loosen their feathers after death.

● The Vegetarian Society and Animal Aid have more information available on factory farming. See page 39 for address details.

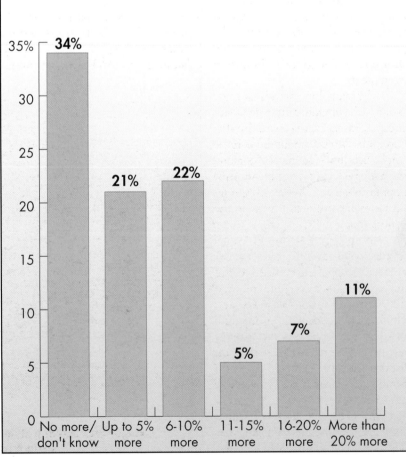

NOP poll for the Danish Bacon and Meat Council

Percentage of customers willing to pay more for meat/food produced by 'cruelty-free' methods:

Category	Percentage
No more/don't know	34%
Up to 5% more	21%
6-10% more	22%
11-15% more	5%
16-20% more	7%
More than 20% more	11%

Vegetarianism

Information from the Meat and Livestock Commission

Official Government statistics *prove* that meat consumption has remained fairly static for the past thirty years. Meat consumption is not decreasing – Government statistics show that in 1990 people in this country consumed 65.4 kg per head whereas in 1970 it was 64.2 kg.

However, what has changed is the mix of meats we eat – and more is consumed out of the home in restaurants, such as steakhouses.

During the past thirty years the number of vegetarians has been carefully tracked and new figures from leading independent research companies show a reduction in the number of non meat-eaters from three per cent to two per cent. It is a complete fallacy that vegetarianism is growing.

Some surveys have indicated that vegetarians are at less risk of heart disease than the average of the population. But this has never been shown to be due to their abstention from meat.

Although long-standing vegetarians, who are generally from higher social classes, are more health conscious (they take more exercise, smoke less and eat more fruit and vegetables) than the general population, meat-eaters with similar lifestyles are also healthier than the general population.

Recent surveys of the very small number of young people (mainly girls) who have temporarily turned vegetarian suggest some may be deficient in vital minerals and vitamins found in meat, e.g. iron and vitamin B12. Iron absorption from meat is at least twice that from plant foods and vitamin B12 is not normally found in foods of vegetable origin.

However, independent research shows many of the few youngsters who 'go vegetarian' do not understand the full definition of the word vegetarian, i.e. they still eat fish or dishes containing meat such as chilli con carne or lasagne.

Meals and snacks which do not contain meat or fish are a long established part of British cuisine. Ploughman's lunches, cheese and onion pies, macaroni cheese, spaghetti and baked beans on toast have been consumed by meat-eaters without any sense of being 'vegetarian' for years. Vegetable curries were on the menus of Indian restaurants from their first beginnings here.

The vast majority of children eat meat

It is quite natural that the growth of new meat dishes (over four new red meat products per week were launched in 1991) and meat cuts has been mirrored by additions to the ranges of non-meat or fish products.

Most of these are prepared and sold from shelves or cabinets which contain an overwhelming preponderance of products and packets which contain meat or fish. Food marked as being suitable for vegetarians is helpful for potential vegetarian customers but it does not indicate a growth in vegetarianism.

In 1991 there was the development and launch of 210 new products containing red meat – this is a sign of a positive industry. 'New foods' such as burgers, kebabs, meat curries and meat lasagne have all become part of the British diet over the past 10 years.

The vast majority of children eat meat, albeit in products that particularly appeal to them such as burgers, hot dogs, sausages and mince. Independent catering studies regularly show that children's favourite meal is a burger.

© Meat and Livestock Commission
June, 1996

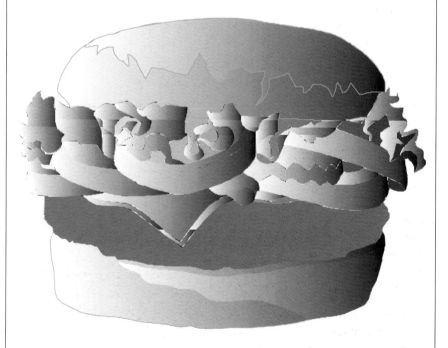

Independent catering studies regularly show that children's favourite meal is a burger

BSE and human health

An National Farmers Union (NFU) briefing paper

The nature of BSE and its origin

Bovine spongiform encephalopathy (BSE) is one of a group of diseases collectively known as transmissible spongiform encephalopathies (TSE) and is a disease affecting cattle. Other forms of TSE include scrapie in sheep and Creutzfeldt-Jakob disease (CJD) in humans.

BSE was identified as a new disease in November 1986 and was made notifiable in June 1988. Farmers receive compensation for any animals which are compulsorily destroyed because they are believed to be affected with BSE.

This is a food-borne infection and probably originated when changes in rendering procedures during the early 1980s failed to inactivate scrapie in infected sheep tissues during the manufacture of meat and bone meal which was subsequently incorporated in cattle feed. Most cases in the epidemic are due to the subsequent recycling of infected cattle material in compound feed, allowing cattle-to-cattle infection.

BSE is not contagious nor is there any direct evidence that the disease is transmitted from the cow to its calf.

Progress of the disease

Cases of BSE in cattle reached a peak in late 1992 and since then have been falling rapidly.

Just under 33,500 farms in Great Britain, representing 35% of herds with adult breeding cattle, have experienced at least one case of BSE. The incidence of the disease is higher in the dairy herd (59%) than in the specialist suckler herd (15%) largely because dairy cows tend to be fed more compound feeds.

Representing Farmers and Growers

Human health controls

Control measures designed to prevent material which may contain the BSE agent from entering the food chain are purely precautionary. In his statement in the House of Commons on 20 March 1996, based on advice from the Government's independent scientific advisors, the Spongiform Encephalopathy Advisory Committee (SEAC), the Secretary of State for Health stated:

'There remains no scientific proof that BSE can be transmitted to man by beef.'

The principal human health control measures are the slaughter and destruction of suspected cases of BSE, introduced in August 1988, and the ban on the use of specified bovine material (SBM) for human consumption, introduced in November 1989.

The SBM are certain tissues which must be removed from all cattle at slaughter. They are the head (excluding tongue), spinal cord, spleen and tonsils of cattle over 6

Confirmed Cases of BSE in Great Britain			
1986	7	1992	36,681
1987	435	1993	34,370
1988	2,184	1994	23,944
1989	7,137	1995	14,186
1990	14,181	1996	2,098
1991	25,032		(at 31 May)

Source: MAFF

months old and the intestines and thymus of cattle of any age.

All these measures remove from human food all tissues in which infectivity may be found in cattle *whether they have clinical disease or appear healthy*. These controls are rigorously enforced by the Meat Hygiene Service and by local authorities, and monitored by the State Veterinary Service.

As a further market support and consumer confidence-building measure, all cattle over 30 months of age are removed from the human food chain and destroyed.

The safety of offal

Offal, other than certain of the SBM, has never been found to contain any traces of BSE infection. Since all SBM is removed at the point of slaughter, consumers can be reassured that any offal on sale to the public is safe.

The safety of processed meats

There have been suggestions that processed meats such as pies and burgers may pose a greater risk to consumers than cuts of meat. There is no reason at all why processed meats should be any less safe than cuts of meat. Even where offal is among the ingredients there is no cause for concern.

The UK's BSE control measures have been endorsed by the World Health Organisation of the United Nations and the Scientific Veterinary Committee of the European Union.

BSE and Creutzfeldt-Jakob disease

The incidence of CJD in the UK is similar to other countries some of which have had no cases of BSE. CJD has been recorded in life-long vegetarians and, while rare, in teenagers in other countries as well as the UK. However, scientists now believe they have identified a new strain of CJD in younger cases in this country.

SEAC, in its latest recommendations, has concluded that there is no direct evidence of a link between BSE and the new disease pattern of CJD which has been identified in 11 cases which have occurred in people under the age of 42.

Although there is no direct evidence of a link, SEAC has

Cases per million population	
UK, 1994	0.93
Netherlands, 1994	1.04
Germany, 1994	0.73
France, 1994	0.81
Israel, 1963-87	0.91
New Zealand, 1980-89	0.88

concluded that the most likely explanation at present is that these cases are linked to exposure to BSE

before the introduction of the SBM ban in 1989.

If its recommendations are implemented, SEAC concluded that 'the risk from eating beef is now likely to be extremely small'. The measures now in place in fact go beyond these recommendations.

The Chief Medical Officer has also stated that 'the scientific evidence for the risks of developing CJD in those eating meat in childhood has not changed as a result of these new findings'.

Danger: meat & milk!

Patrick Holford, Founder of the Institute for Optimum Nutrition, begins his assault on the mainstays of the Western diet – meat and dairy – with an examination of the health risks associated with BSE and the widespread use of 'farmaceutical' products

The average person in Britain consumes over 907g of meat and 2.27 litres of milk a week. The traditional view is that meat and milk are good for you – high in protein, calcium and iron. But the BSE (Bovine Spongiform Encephalopathy) scare has fuelled a growing concern that modern farming methods have gone too far. More and more people are becoming vegetarian and vegan.

Leaving moral issues aside, there are a number of safety issues causing grave concern among scientists. For meat, these include the use of antibiotics, sex and growth hormones, pesticide 'dips' and BSE.

BSE – a serious risk?

According to Professor of Microbiology, Richard Lacey: 'The honest answer is nobody knows it isn't.' What is known is that BSE is caused by an infectious agent, becomes noticeable in older animals, and has a relatively long incubation period. In cattle, the oldest animals affected are knackered dairy cows, slaughtered when unable to produce milk profitably. Their meat is the cheapest, the most likely to end up

in beefburgers and other processed meat products (including 'pork' sausages and 'lamb' stock), and the most likely to be from a BSE-infected animal. Ministry of Agriculture, Fisheries and Food (MAFF) studies have shown that BSE-infected meat can infect most animal species – including monkeys and pigs, whose tissues have infectious susceptibility similar to human tissue. While the Government and meat industry say that milk carries no risk, few serious studies have been undertaken. 'Milk from BSE-infected animals does appear to carry a lower risk, but not a zero risk,' says Lacey.

A disease similar to BSE, Creutzfeldt-Jakob Disease (CJD), exists in humans. The death toll from CJD is small, but rising – especially among farmers and other workers in the meat industry. Officially, there were only 54 cases last year, but because the disease is not notifiable by law the true numbers are not known. Unofficially the numbers are estimated by some to exceed 2,000 per year.

The million dollar question is: does eating BSE-infected meat cause CJD and, if so, how long is the incubation period? The Institute for Optimum Nutrition (ION) asked Professor Lacey this question in 1992. He said: 'There's an 80% chance we'll be vulnerable and the timing is likely to be in 20 years' time. The beginning of the epidemic is likely to be seen when dementia starts to occur early in life, among 20 to 30-year-olds, in ten or so years' time.'

Last year saw three reported cases of CJD in young people, the youngest being 16. Stephen Churchill, aged 19, died within 12 months of contracting the disease. Michelle Bowen, who worked in a butcher's shop, died at the age of 29. A *World*

Veganism

Questions and answers

What is a vegan?

A vegan's diet is *free of any products derived from animals* – including meat, fish, poultry, eggs, (non-human) animal milk, honey, and their derivatives. But being a vegan doesn't only mean avoiding foods; it's an exciting venture into a world of tasty ingredients, with the added know-ledge that no cow or chicken has had to suffer to produce the meal on your dinner plate. Veganism borrows from the best of many cuisines, and today it's easy to buy vegan food, from soya yoghurts to veggie burgers, and from tofu mayonnaise to soya ice cream. Wonderful cakes and biscuits can be made without resorting to using even one egg!

What do vegans eat for a balanced diet?

The Vegan Society recommends a varied approach with regular use of foods from the following groups: pulses, whole grains and seeds, fresh vegetables – including green leafy ones, and fresh and dried fruits. With such wholesome and simple ingre-dients a delicious variety of meals can be made. There are also many foods that can be bought in super-markets suitable for vegans to use. The Vegan Society produces a paperback book called *The Animal Free Shopper* listing such products. See the sheet 'Living Without Cruelty', published by the Vegan Society, for further details of essential nutrients and their food source.

Isn't a vegan diet deficient in some nutrients?

There isn't a single nutrient which a balanced and varied vegan diet cannot provide, and doctors who warn of painful monthly injections or instant anaemia are talking through their hats! However,

being a vegan does require understanding a little about vegan sources of those essential nutrients. It's no good giving up meat, milk and eggs, and surviving on tea and bread or chips and Coke.

What about protein?

Plant protein has been commonly thought of as second class protein because it was of a poor quality. This is rubbish and plant proteins contain all the essential amino acids necessary for good health. Is protein-combining necessary? Until fairly recently, vegans were advised to combine two 'complementary' protein foods at each meal (i.e. combining grains and pulses or nuts/seeds and pulses), to be sure of getting the combination of amino acids which the body needs. However, research has shown that this isn't necessary after all and that eating a varied wholefood diet throughout the day will provide the body with the correct amino acids to remain healthy. For further details

on protein please see the Vegan Society's information sheet on this subject.

Are there any problems obtaining the necessary vitamins for a healthy diet?

A wholefood vegan diet contains lots of vitamins, especially A, the B complex, C, E and K. Like meat-eaters and vegetarians, vegans obtain most of their vitamin D by the action of sunlight on the skin. Some people think that vitamin B12 presents a problem, but it is easily available in fortified products such as Marmite, textured vegetable meat substitutes and some soya milks and vegan margarines. Vitamin B12 deficiency is rare in vegans. There is some evidence that people who grow their own vegetables obtain this vitamin (which is really a bacteria) from the vegetables and that some people have the ability to produce their own B12 in their own bodies.

Don't vegans get anaemic?

Despite scare stories in the media, vegan diets contain more than twice the recommended amount of iron and studies show that the iron status of vegans is usually normal, and iron deficiency is no more common than in the general population. Although plant iron is less well-absorbed than iron from meat, and the fibre and phytate in plant foods may interfere slightly with absorption, the amounts of vitamin C eaten by most vegans help overcome any possible problem in this area. For further information on iron see the Vegan Society's information sheet on this subject.

Doesn't a vegan diet lack calcium?

There have been no reports of calcium deficiency in vegans. This seems to be because there are other factors in a plant-based diet which allow vegans to make the best use of calcium in their food. For example, a diet high in protein, especially meat, causes the body to lose calcium. As vegans eat no meat and their protein intake is moderate, their bodies retain more calcium. Similarly, some research suggests that boron, a mineral found especially in fruits and vegetables, encourages the body to make use of calcium in the diet. Foods rich in calcium include tofu, almonds, brazils, soya flour, spinach, molasses, sesame and sunflower seeds (and especially spreads made from them), and parsley. For further information on calcium see the Vegan Society's information sheet on this subject.

What are the health benefits of a vegan diet?

Research involving human 'guinea pigs' is gradually revealing the health benefits of veganism. Low in fat, especially saturated fat, and cholesterol-free; high in fibre and complex carbohydrates; low in salt; and rich in vitamins A and C, vegan diets have much to offer the health-conscious. Vegans are less at risk of high blood pressure, heart disease, cancer of the breast and colon (two of the most common cancers), gallstones, diverticular disease, haemorrhoids, diabetes and kidney stones. Some doctors have prescribed vegan diets for treating high blood pressure, angina, rheumatoid arthritis and asthma, and several patients have been able to give up drugs which they were taking for those conditions.

● The above is an extract from a series of information sheets produced by the Vegan Society. See page 39 for address details.

© The Vegan Society

Vegan concerns

If you're concerned about your health, the well-being of the planet and the avoidance of animal suffering, then a closer look at the vegan diet is for you . . .

Health

A vegan diet is high in fibre, vitamins and minerals but low in cholesterol, saturated fat and salt. This is achieved by eating only plant foods such as nuts, beans, cereals, vegetables and fruits. Research involving human volunteers has shown that those on such a diet are at less risk of high blood pressure, breast and bowel cancer, diabetes, arthritis, varicose veins, heart disease, piles and kidney stones. Generations of vegans have demonstrated both the adequacy and health advantages of a vegan diet.

The planet

Currently eight times as much land is cultivated than is necessary to support people living on plant foods alone; 7/8 is used to sustain farm animals. Clearly, passing plant material through animals is a highly inefficient use of scarce resources. Animal-based agriculture is a major contributor to environmental destruction e.g. acid rain, deforestation, soil erosion, global warming and water pollution.

Animals

Humans share a common bond with animals – the ability to feel pain. Rearing animals for food, whether factory-farmed or free-range, cannot be separated from the infliction of pain and suffering. Every year hundreds of millions of animals are killed for meat, while dairy products involve cows in an unending cycle of pregnancy, lactation and removal of their calves within a few days of birth. The majority of dairy calves are destined for slaughter, conversion into prime beef, or export for veal production using the 'crate' system (banned in the UK).

If you would like to make a positive and practical contribution towards improving your health, saving the planet and reducing animal suffering by adopting a vegan diet, the Vegan Society – an educational charity – can help.

● For more information about the society and the vegan diet write to the Vegan Society. See page 39 for address details.

© The Vegan Society

Summary of Realeat polls 1984–1995

% of population	'84	'85	'86	'87	'88	'90	'93	'95
Vegetarians	2.1	2.6	2.7	3.0	3.0	3.7	4.3	4.5
Avoid red meat	1.9	2.6	3.1	3.6	5.5	6.3	6.5	7.3
Eating less meat	n/a	30	35	33	35	43	40	n/a

© The Vegetarian Society

ADDITIONAL RESOURCES

You might like to contact the following organisations for further information. Due to the increasing cost of postage, many organisations cannot respond to enquiries unless they receive a stamped, addressed envelope.

British Chicken Information Service
126-128 Cromwell Road
London
SW7 4ET
Tel: 0171 373 7757

Produces an information pack for teachers. They do not produce student packs.

British Nutrition Foundation (BNF)
High Holborn House
52-54 High Holborn
London WC1V 6RQ
Tel: 0171 404 6504
Fax: 0171 404 6747

The (BNF) is an independent charity which provides reliable information and advice on nutrition and related health matters. They produce a wide range of leaflets, briefing papers and books. Ask for their publications list.

Compassion in World Farming (CIWF) Trust
5a Charles Street
Petersfield
Hampshire GU32 3EH
Tel: 01730 268070
Fax: 01730 260791

Campaigns for an end to cruel factory farming systems. They publish an information pack, magazines and reports on animal welfare issues.

Health Education Authority
Hamilton House
Mabledon Place
London WC2H 9TX
Tel: 0171 3833 833

Provides free legal advice for people on all health issues. They publish a wide range of leaflets on health-related topics. For information about their publications phone Customer Service on 01235 465565.

Meat & Livestock Commission
PO Box 44
Winterhill House
Snowdon Drive
Milton Keynes
MK6 1AX
Tel: 01908 677577
Fax: 01908 609826

Produces an information pack on various aspects of the meat and livestock industry.

Milk Marketing Board
Press Office
Thames Ditton
Surrey KT7 0EL
Tel: 0181 910 4343

National Farmers' Union
Public Affairs Department
22 Long Acre
London WC2E 9LY
Tel: 0171 331 7200
Fax: 0171 235 3526

Produces an information pack on various aspects of the farming industry.

Royal Society for the Prevention of Cruelty to Animals (RSPCA)
The Causeway, Horsham
West Sussex RH12 1HG
Tel: 01403 264181
Fax: 01403 241048

Produces a wide range of leaflets and other materials on animal welfare issues. Please contact the Enquiries Service.

The Food Commission
3rd Floor
5-11 Worship Street
London EC2A 2BH
Tel: 0171 628 7774
Fax: 0171 628 0817

Provides education, information and research on nutrition, diet, health and food production. Runs various educational and research campaigns, publishes *The Food Magazine* and other publications.

The Jewish Vegetarian and Ecological Society
855 Finchley Road
London
NW11 8LX
Tel: 0181 455 0692

Health, nutrition, cookery, books, restaurants, fitness as well as coverage of general interest to vegetarianism.

The Vegan Society Ltd
7 Battle Road
St Leonards on Sea
East Sussex TN37 7AA
Tel: 01424 427393
Fax: 01424 427393

Publish *The Vegan* which includes information on animal rights/ welfare, veganism, land use, new vegan products, green issues, nutrition and health. The society produces magazines, factsheets and a wide range of other literature. Ask for their publications list.

The Vegetarian Society of the United Kingdom Ltd
Parkdale
Dunham Road
Altrincham
Cheshire WA14 4QT
Tel: 0161 928 0793
Fax: 0161 926 9182

The society produces magazines, factsheets and a wide range of other literature. Ask for their publications list.

VIVA!
PO Box 212
Crewe
Cheshire CW1 4SD
Tel: 01270 522 500
Fax: 01270 522 511

Publish 12 Viva Guides. They also have a new book published in September 1996, *The Livewire Guide to Going, Being and Staying Veggie* by Juliet Gellatley. Published by The Women's Press.

ACKNOWLEDGEMENTS

The publisher is grateful for permission to reproduce the following material.

While every care has been taken to trace and acknowledge copyright, the publisher tenders its apology for any accidental infringement or where copyright has proved untraceable. The publisher would be pleased to come to a suitable arrangement in any such case with the rightful owner.

An overview
The practice of vegetarianism, © British Nutrition Association.

Chapter One: Food for thought
Farmfacts – animal transport, © Compassion in World Farming, *The transportation of live animals*, © National Farmers' Union, February 1995, *Farmfacts – factory farming*, © Compassion in World Farming, *Animal welfare*, © Meat and Livestock Commission, *Animal welfare*, © National Farmers' Union, June 1995, *Reading the welfare labels*, © Living Earth & The Food Magazine, April/June 1995, *Freedom Food has arrived!*, © Freedom Foods Ltd, *Planet on a plate*, © Viva!, *Feeding the world*, © Meat and Livestock Commission, June 1994, *Meat – the facts*, © Meat and Livestock Commission, *Getting to the meat of the matter*, © The Vegetarian Society.

Chapter Two: A question of diet
So you want to be a vegetarian?, © Essentials, April 1996, *Introduction – what the experts say*, © Meat and Livestock Commission, June 1996, *Why go vegetarian?*, © The Vegetarian Society and Animal Aid, *Vegetarianism*, © Meat and Livestock Commission, June 1996, *BSE and human health*, © Meat and Livestock Commission, June, 1996, *Danger: meat and milk!*, © The Vegan, Spring 1996, *Background to BSE*, © Meat and Livestock Commission, *Veggie Burghers*, © The Telegraph plc, London, 1996, *Alternatives to meat*, © The Food Magazine, Oct/Dec 1995, *Why parents get muddled*, © Viva!, *Veganism*, © The Vegan Society, *Vegan concerns*, © The Vegan Society.

Photographs and Illustrations
Pages 7, 16: Katherine Flemng / Folio Collective, pages 15, 21, 36: Ken Pyne, page 30: Andrew Smith / Folio Collective.

Craig Donnellan
Cambridge
September, 1996